PELICAN BOOKS
A153
COMMON WILD FLOWERS
BY JOHN HUTCHINSON

COMMON
WILD FLOWERS

BY JOHN HUTCHINSON

WITH 216 ILLUSTRATIONS

PUBLISHED BY
PENGUIN BOOKS
WEST DRAYTON · MIDDLESEX

First published May 1945
Revised Edition July 1946
Reprinted 1948

Made and Printed in Great Britain for Penguin Books, Limited,
by Richard Clay and Company, Ltd., Bungay, Suffolk.
Photogravure Plates by Clarke and Sherwell, Ltd., Northampton.

INTRODUCTION

THIS book has been written expressly for those people—men, women and children—who have little or no knowledge of botany, and who want to learn the names and a little about the common wild flowers of the countryside. No doubt the majority of those who use the book will be content to match the wild flowers they find with the drawings. But others—and it is hoped they will not be few—will see more than the pretty posy and look a little further into the structure of the flowers. This is an interesting and fascinating study which will soon bring its own reward in a

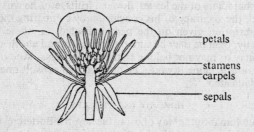

petals

stamens
carpels

sepals

more extended knowledge of plants, and perhaps lead on to the use of the many excellent *Floras*, a selection of which is given on page x. With this object in view, therefore, particular attention has been paid to the illustration of dissections of important parts of the flowers, fruits and seeds, such as may be seen with the aid of a penknife and hand-lens. These usually exhibit the important characters of the genus and family. In the general sketch of the plant, perspective has as a rule been neglected in order to show clearly the shapes of leaves and other features which are often of great importance for recognising the species.

If we wish to use the book intelligently, however, and not merely search mechanically through the drawings for the plants we wish to name, it will be necessary to learn something about the structure of a simple kind of flower, in order to use the key on page xi. For this purpose we cannot do better than pull to pieces the flower of a common buttercup as illustrated above. The five outermost green parts are the *sepals* (collectively called the *calyx*), the five yellow organs are, of course, the *petals* (forming the *corolla*) with a nectary at the base; then we come to the numerous *stamens*, consisting of a stalk (*filament*) and pollen-carrier (*anther*), and finally a number of small green parts in the middle and arranged in a spiral, the *carpels*. These, in the buttercup, are free from one another, but in most other flowers they are united together to form a single *ovary*. The stamens with their pollen represent the male element of the flower, and the carpels or ovary with their immature seeds, the ovules, the female part, and the latter produces the fruit and seed. Having performed this operation, we should be fairly well qualified to use the simple type of key beginning on page xi, which has been, provided to enable the observer to "run down" the majority of the really common and widely distributed wild flowers which he is likely to find. Having followed the key to the place indicated by the characters of the leaves, flowers, fruits, etc., he will be able to check the accuracy of his conclusion by comparing the figure and description given on the page indicated. If these do not quite tally, then he may be sure that he has found another plant, which may or may not belong to the same genus. And in order to find out its name it would be necessary to consult one of the *Floras* indicated.

HOW TO USE THE KEY

To put him into the way of using the key, the Buttercup may be given a trial. As it is a herb with net-veined leaves, it obviously belongs to Part II of the key on p. xii. In that group, as it is neither a tree nor a shrub, nor woody in any way, it does not belong to the group covered by line 1, but agrees with that described under 1a (p. xv). Then it has not a head of flowers, as described in line 37 (p. xv), so belongs to line 37a (p. xviii). But the flowers are not in umbels, so line 63 (p. xviii) can be bypassed, and it obviously belongs to the contrasting characters at line 63a (p. xix). As the leaves are alternate or all from the base of the plant, the butter-cup agrees with the characters given under line 75 (p. xix). Then the chase is getting warm, for the female part is composed of several separate carpels (line 76), the petals are not united (line 77), the leaves have no stipules (line 78), and are not thick and fleshy (line 79), the sepals are not coloured (line 80), and there are 5 petals and 5 sepals, so it must be, or at any rate is very probably, *Ranunculus* (figs. 69, 70).

After a little practice the reader will probably soon begin to recognise related plants or *families* of flowering plants. In the case of the Rose family, for example, called *Rosaceae* after the genus *Rosa*, it will be observed (figures 4–18) that the female part or ovary of the flower is usually described as being composed of free carpels, which when ripe contain the seeds. The fact that the carpels are free from one another, associated with other features, is therefore one, but only one, of the spotting characters by which the Rose family may be recognised.

Again, it will be very noticeable on looking over figures 142–170 that the apparently single flower is in reality an aggregation of flowers into a head (*capitulum*). And with a few exceptions it will be found that most plants with a similar head of flowers belong to the Daisy family, *Compositae*, and we soon learn to recognise that family, especially if we have also seen that the anthers are joined together around the style.

Some flowers are hardly recognisable as such because they are very small and have no petals. These are often crowded together into catkins, which, like the head of the *Compositae*, is a particular kind of *inflorescence*. Most people know at least one kind of inflorescence, a *spike*, which suggests at once a stiff dense collection of flowers.

The notes accompanying the drawings are confined to a short, general, and very simple description of the usual form of the species as it is met with in a wild state, and little or no mention is made of varieties or forms which occur in some cases. Variation in the colour of the flowers, however, is usually noted. In addition, room has been found for a few facts relating to the biology of the flower, particularly regarding pollination in examples which seem sufficiently obvious to the observer. The pollination of flowers is a subject of great importance to the bee-keeper, the fruit-grower, and the seedsman. In this country Charles Darwin was the foremost investigator. And there is still a good deal more to be learned.

In addition, where space permits, a few notes are added on the uses to which some of our wild plants are put, including those which are poisonous. Very few of them are now exploited, and their local use as remedies has almost completely died out, since there is a chemist's shop in nearly every village. During the war, however, when we were more or less cut off from external supplies, interest in them was revived. In consequence, the common foxglove, the henbane, the belladonna, and the autumn crocus have played their part. Even the despised nettle has provided a useful fibre and has been used for the extraction of chlorophyll, whilst the rose hip, rich in vitamin C, has helped greatly as an antiscorbutic in the absence of oranges. For example, five hundred tons of rose-hips were collected from hedgerows during 1943, sufficient to manufacture two and a half million bottles of National Rose Hip Syrup, and considered to be equivalent in Vitamin C content to twenty-five million oranges. Other plants of less importance in the war effort were broom-tops, burdock leaves and roots, coltsfoot leaves, comfrey roots and leaves, dandelion roots, elder flowers and fruits, hawthorn berries, lime-tree flowers, raspberry leaves, valerian root, and wormwood, all being the source of a wide variety of medicines.

The arrangement of the families represented by the plants illustrated follows the author's own system of classification, which aims at a sequence of increasing specialisation.* This is not very difficult to understand. First come the conifers, of which we have only three. These are considered to be more primitive than the remainder of the flowering plants. Then all those plants are grouped together which usually have *net-veined leaves* and *two seed-leaves* (Dicotyledons), and the remainder, with *parallel-veined leaves* and only *one seed leaf* (Monocotyledons), come last; the latter include the lily and orchid families, etc., the sedges, and grasses. The Dicotyledons are further arranged into two main groups. First come the trees and shrubs and some herbs related to them, and secondly the purely herbaceous plants and a few related slightly woody plants. The first group embraces figures 4 to 67, and the second figures 68 to 196, whilst the Monocotyledons will be found from figure 197 to the end. The reader with some knowledge of botany may recognise that the families which exhibit the most primitive floral structure are placed first, and the most advanced come last in each of these groups, the grass family being regarded as one of the most highly specialised.

The Latin names of the plants included in the book are in accordance with the International Rules of Botanical Nomenclature, so far as ascertained. A departure from common practice has been made, however, in the case of some of the names of the species. These have all been printed with a small initial letter, as is usual in zoology. Botanists generally spell certain specific names with a capital letter, especially those derived from an old genus name, and those named after persons. Thus *Sorbus Aucuparia* L., the Rowan tree, is usually so printed

* J. Hutchinson, *Families of Flowering Plants* (Macmillan, London), Vol. I (1926), Vol. II (1934).

because *Aucuparia* is an old genus name. The " L." after the Latin name indicates that Linnaeus, the famous Swedish botanist, often spoken of as the " father of modern botany," was responsible for giving the name to the tree. The majority of the species of our commoner British plants were named by Linnaeus, as most of them are also found in Sweden. In a few cases the " L." is included in brackets after the Latin name, and the name, or abbreviated name, of another botanist follows it. This indicates that though Linnaeus first described the species, the latter is now placed under a different genus name. An example is the Stork's Bill, *Erodium cicutarium* (L.) L'Hérit. Linnaeus described it as *Geranium cicutarium*, and it was later transferred by the French botanist L'Héritier to *Erodium*.

Owing to the limitation of space, it has been possible to include few except the most common species. Some groups of plants, such as the Sedges, Grasses, the many kinds of Brambles, Roses, and Hawkweeds, though including some that are very common, are mostly difficult to distinguish except by intensive study, and have therefore been omitted. Nearly all the species included occur in the 112 vice-counties of Druce's *Comital Flora*, and a few of the less common have been put in either because of some special interest or of their economic importance. With one or two exceptions the illustrations are original and have been drawn by the author specially for this book.

Our wild plants are a precious heritage. They should be preserved as much as possible, and rare and local kinds should on no account be dug up. Avoid trampling on the leaves of plants, especially bluebells, as this weakens or kills them.

The author is greatly indebted to Sir Edward J. Salisbury, F.R.S., Director of the Royal Botanic Gardens, Kew, at whose suggestion the book has been prepared, and for friendly help and encouragement, and to those who have supplied photographs, especially Messrs. Heath and Heather of St. Albans, who own the copyright of some of them.

The photographs used in the book were kindly supplied by the following: Miss Anne Jackson (Heartsease, Silverweed, Cowslips, Ramsons, Blackberry, Lesser Celandine, Sloe, Honeysuckle, and Butterbur); Miss D. G. C. Long (Wood Betony, Yarrow, Centaury, Wild Carrot, and Black Horehound); Mr. E. J. Bedford (Tansy and Wild Violets); Mr. E. Richardson (Henbane and Marsh Marigold); Mr. G. F. Unwin (Foxgloves); Sir Edward J. Salisbury (Buckbean); Mr. H. Bastin (Meadow Sweet)

Hanover House, Kew.

BOOKS RECOMMENDED FOR
FURTHER STUDY

Among a great number of excellent botanical text-books, the
following recent works are recommended for those who wish to
pursue the subject further :—

1. Hooker, *Student's Flora of the British Islands* * (Macmillan,
   1937).
2. Fitch and Smith, *Illustrations* to Bentham and Hooker's
   Handbook of the British Flora ed. 7 (L. Reeve and Co.,
   Ashford, Kent, 1924).
3. Butcher and Strudwick, *Further Illustrations of British Plants*
   (L. Reeve and Co., 1930).
4. Skene, *The Biology of Flowering Plants* (Sidgwick and Jackson,
   Ltd., London, 1924).
5. Fritsch and Salisbury, *Plant Form and Function* (G. Bell and
   Sons, Ltd., London, 1943).

The most comprehensive work on flower pollination is Knuth,
Handbook of Flower Pollination, English translation by Ainsworth
Davis (Clarendon Press, Oxford, 1908).

* 3rd edition of 1884, reprinted in 1937 ; there is no up-to-date
British *Flora*.

KEY FOR NAMING COMMON
FLOWERING PLANTS

(For how to use the Key, see p. vi)

A key to determine common plants is given in the following pages and is divided up into three parts as follows :—

Part I is very short, and deals only with Conifer plants (*Coniferae*) (known as *Gymnosperms*, because their ovules are not enclosed in an ovary); to this group belong the Yew, Pine and Juniper.

Part II is by far the largest, and most of the more common flowering plants in Britain (except Sedges and Grasses) belong to it. The leaves are net-veined, the bundles (vascular) of the stem are arranged in a circle, and the seedling has two seed-leaves when it starts to grow. These plants are known as *Dicotyledons*.

Part III (on page xxix) is quite a small group, and would include the Sedges and Grasses if they were illustrated; the leaves in this group have parallel veins (nerves), are usually long and narrow, the bundles (vascular) in the stem are scattered (not in a circle or circles) and the seedling has only one seed-leaf. These are known as *Monocotyledons*. The common plants of this group are the Bluebell, Arum, Wild Onion, Iris, and most people know these more or less. The user of this book will therefore be mainly concerned with part II.

Key, Part I

1 Leaves borne singly on the shoots though rather crowded, not very sharp pointed; male and female "flowers" on separate plants; seed ("fruit") surrounded by a fleshy red cup-like structure (aril); Yew tree (FIG. 1)　　*Taxus*

1a Leaves needle-like and borne in pairs on very short shoots with scales at their base; male and female "flowers" (cones) on the same plant; seeds winged, borne in cones with woody overlapping scales; Pine tree (FIG. 2)　*Pinus*

1b Leaves arranged in threes and with sharp prickly points; male and female cones usually on different plants, borne in the axils of the leaves; "fruit" fleshy like a berry; Juniper shrub (FIG. 3) .　.　.　.　.　　*Juniperus*

1 **Trees and shrubs or shrublets (rarely climbers) with woody stems and branches persisting for more than one season (to p. xv):**

2 Leaves divided into 3 or more separate leaflets:

3 Stamens numerous (more than 10):

4 Tree with flat corymbs of cream-white flowers with petals and red or yellowish-red fruits; Rowan or Mountain Ash (FIG. 8) . . . . *Sorbus*

4a Bush with large pink flowers and prickly stems; Wild Rose (FIG. 9) . . . . *Rosa*

4b Climber; without petals but with white sepals; fruits separate, with long feathery tails; Traveller's Joy (FIG. 73) . . . . *Clematis*

3b Stamens 10, united into a tube; Broom (FIG. 20) *Cytisus*

3c Stamens 5; fruits small and black, numerous in a flat-topped cluster (corymb); stems with broad soft pith; Elder (FIG. 64) . . . . *Sambucus*

3d Stamens 2; fruits dry and expanded into a wing at the top; wood hard throughout; Ash tree (FIG. 60) *Fraxinus*

2a Leaves not divided into separate leaflets:

5 Leaves evergreen, with coarse sharp prickly lobes, thick and leathery; berries small and red; hard nearly white wood; Holly tree (FIG. 54) . . . . . *Ilex*

5a Leaves not as above, rarely evergreen:

6 *Leaves alternate on the shoots (to p. xiv):*

7 Flowers in catkins (i.e. slender, narrow, and pendulous) or in dense spikes covered with small bracts; no petals (to p. xiii):

8 Flowers in slender pendulous catkins; trees:

9 Leaves rather deeply pinnately lobed; fruit an acorn surrounded by a cuplike scaly involucre; Oak trees (FIG. 34) . . . . . . *Quercus*

9a Leaves at most coarsely toothed:

10 Leaves rounded or ovate, pointed at the apex:

11 Leaves heart-shaped (cordate) at the base, doubly toothed; fruit a nut surrounded by a cup-like green jagged involucre; bark not white; Nut tree (FIG. 32) . . . . . . *Corylus*

11a Leaves wedge-shaped at the base; fruit a small winged nut; stems with whitish peeling bark; Birch tree (FIG. 30) . . . . . *Betula*

10a Leaves hollowed out at the apex, wedge-shaped at the base; female flowers arranged in dense cone-like structures covered with overlapping bracts; Alder tree, grows near water (FIG. 31)

Alnus

8a Flowers in dense but not pendulous spikes:

12 Small shrubs growing in marshy places, with narrow toothed gland-dotted leaves; stamens inconspicuous; Bog Myrtle (FIG. 29) . . *Myrica*

12a Small trees, with rather broad leaves; male spikes with very conspicuous stamens with slender filaments; Willow tree (FIG. 28) . . . *Salix*

7a Flowers neither in catkins nor in dense spikes; sometimes in rather dense clusters:

13 Flowers arranged in an umbel, their stalks in a cluster arising from one point like the ribs of an umbrella:

14 Common flower-stalk with a large narrow bract joined to it about the middle; leaves rounded and toothed; Lime tree (FIG. 43) . . . . *Tilia*

14a Common flower-stalk without a bract as described above:

15 Leaves evergreen, either entire or rather coarsely lobed, but not toothed; flowers small, appearing in autumn; Ivy (FIG. 58) . . . . *Hedera*

15a Leaves deciduous, finely toothed or rather deeply lobed:

16 Flowers very conspicuous, pink or white:

17 Ovary above the calyx (FIG. 5) . . . *Prunus*

17a Ovary below the calyx:

18 Leaves at most toothed; Crab tree (FIG. 6)

Malus

18a Leaves rather deeply lobed and toothed; Hawthorn (FIG. 7) . . . . . *Crataegus*

16a Flowers very small and green; Buckthorn (FIG. 56) . . . . *Rhamnus*

13a Flowers not arranged in an umbel as described above:

19 Branches ending in a short spine or hardened tip:

20 Stamens not united into a sheath; flower regular (i.e. may be divided into more than 2 equal parts):

21 Ovary above the calyx; berry blue-black, like a small plum and very sour; Sloe (FIG. 4) *Prunus*

21a Ovary below the calyx; berries small and red;
Hawthorn (FIG. 7) . . . . . *Crataegus*

20a Stamens united into a sheath; flower irregular
(*i.e.* may be divided only into 2 equal halves);
fruit a flat pod; Common Gorse (FIG. 19) *Ulex*

19a Branches not ending in a spine or hardened tip:

22 Flowers without petals:

  23 Leaves slightly toothed; fruits nut-like, triangular,
enclosed in a bristly involucre of bracts; Beech
tree (FIG. 33) . . . . . . *Fagus*

  23a Leaves sharply toothed; fruits thin and flattened;
Elm tree (FIG. 35) . . . . . *Ulmus*

22a Flowers with petals:

  24 Petals free from one another:

    25 Flowers regular (i.e. may be divided into equal
halves in several directions):

      26 Petals conspicuous:

        27 Flowers rather large, like apple blossom; fruit
a small sour apple; stamens numerous;
Crab tree (FIG. 6) . . . . . *Malus*

        27a Flowers small, not like Apple blossom; Haw-
thorn (FIG. 7) . . . . . *Crataegus*

      26a Petals small and inconspicuous, green; stamens
4, opposite the petals; Buckthorn (FIG. 56)
Rhamnus

    25a Flowers irregular (i.e. may be divided into equal
halves in only one direction):

      28 Leaves with large stipules and only 1 leaflet,
sticky with glands; Restharrow (FIG. 21)
Ononis

      28a Leaves with 3 leaflets, not sticky; Broom (FIG.
20) . . . . *Cytisus*

  24a Petals united into a tube; ovary inferior; branches
winged; low shrublet; Bilberry (FIG. 52)
Vaccinium

6a *Leaves opposite or in whorls on the shoots:*

 29 Leaves small and narrow:

  30 Small heath plants with thin wiry branchlets, the petals
united into a tube, pink:

    31 Corolla-tube very short, shorter than the lobes;
common Heather (FIG. 51) . . . *Calluna*

    31a Corolla-tube much longer than the lobes (FIGS. 49, 50)
Erica

30a Not heath-like plants; petals free, soon falling off, yellow; Rock Rose (FIG. 38) . . . *Helianthemum*

29a Leaves rather large; rather large shrubs or climbers, not heath-like:

32 Leaves lobed:

33 Sepals and petals inserted around the ovary; petals free from one another; stamens about 8; fruits divided into 2 winged lobes (" keys "); Maple tree (FIG. 59) . . . . *Acer*

33a Sepals and petals above the ovary; petals united into a short tube; fruit a berry; Guelder Rose (FIG. 66) . . . . . . *Viburnum*

32a Leaves entire or toothed, but not lobed:

34 Sepals, petals and stamens around, but not above the ovary; large disk within the petals; seeds covered with a yellow aril; Spindle tree (FIG. 55) . . . . *Euonymus*

34a Sepals, petals and stamens above the ovary:

35 Flowers regular (i.e. may be divided into more than two equal halves); not climbers:

36 Leaves sharply toothed, clothed with star-shaped hairs below; petals united into a short tube; Wayfaring tree (FIG. 65) . . *Viburnum*

36a Leaves not toothed, clothed with 2-armed (T-shaped) hairs; petals free from one another; Dogwood (FIG. 57) . . . . . *Cornus*

35a Flowers irregular (i.e. may be divided into equal halves in only one direction); climber; Honeysuckle (FIG. 67) . . . . *Lonicera*

1a Herbs with herbaceous stems and branches, if woody, then so only at the base; new stems and shoots usually produced annually:

37 FLOWERS CROWDED TOGETHER INTO A HEAD SURROUNDED BY ONE OR MORE ROWS OF BRACTS FORMING AN INVOLUCRE; PLANTS MOSTLY WITH FLOWER-HEADS MORE OR LESS LIKE THE DAISY (TO P. XVIII):

38 *Anthers of the separate flowers (these often very small) united into a tube around the style (plants of the Daisy family) (to p. xvii):*

39 Flower-heads with flowers of two kinds, both ray- and disk-flowers (to p. xvi):

40 Ray flowers white or pink:

41 Leaves opposite (not all from the root); ray flowers 5; " Kew Weed " (FIG. 147) . . . *Galinsoga*

51a Achenes tapered into a long slender beak; Cat's-ear
(FIG. 163) . . . . *Hypochaeris*
50a Pappus-bristles not feathery as described above:
52 Achenes not tapered into a long beak:
53 Achenes flattened; leaves prickly; Prickly Sow-
thistle (FIGS. 167, 168) . . . . *Sonchus*
53a Achenes not flattened; leaves not prickly:
54 Achenes prominently ribbed; Smooth Crepis (FIG.
165) . . . . *Crepis*
54a Achenes only very slightly ribbed; Mouse-ear
Hawkweed (FIG. 169) . . . *Hieracium*
52a Achenes tapered into a long slender beak, warted;
leaves and flower-heads arising directly from the
rootstock; Dandelion (FIG. 166) . *Taraxacum*
39b Flower-head without any ray flowers, all the flowers
tubular or thread-like:
55 Leaves opposite, usually divided into 3 leaflets; stems
clothed with purplish jointed hairs; Hemp Agrimony (FIG. 142) . . . . . . *Eupatorium*
55a Leaves alternate:
56 Bracts of the involucre jagged at the edge like a comb
(pectinate); Knapweeds (FIGS. 159, 160) *Centaurea*
56a Bracts of the involucre not jagged, though sometimes
spine-tipped:
57 Leaves very prickly or spiny on the margins; Thistles
(FIGS. 161, 162) . . . . . . *Cirsium*
57a Leaves not prickly:
58 Perennials with large rhubarb-like leaves; Butterbur
(FIG. 154) . . . . *Petasites*
58a Annuals or biennials; leaves much-lobed or
divided, not rhubarb-like:
59 Involucral bracts in one main row, with smaller
bracts at the base; Groundsel (FIG. 158) *Senecio*
59a Involucral bracts in several rows:
60 Leaves woolly beneath; flower-heads in a panicle;
Mugwort (FIG. 149) . . . *Artemisia*
60a Leaves not woolly beneath; flower-heads in a flat
corymb; Tansy (FIG. 148) . *Tanacetum*
38a *Anthers of the separate flowers not united around the
style:*
61 Leaves crowded into a bunch, small and narrow; outer
bracts reflexed at the base and forming a sheath
around the stalk; Sea Thrift (FIG. 123) *Armeria*

61a Leaves not as above; outer bracts not forming a reflexed sheath around the stalk:

62 Leaves all from the base of the plant, with more or less
parallel nerves; Plantain (FIG. 124) . *Plantago*

62a Leaves on the stem as well as from the base, mostly
opposite; Devil's bit (FIG. 129) . . *Succisa*

37a FLOWERS NOT CROWDED INTO A HEAD AS DESCRIBED ON P.
XV, OR IF SO NOT SURROUNDED BY AN INVOLUCRE OF
BRACTS:

63 *Flowers arranged in umbels, their stalks radiating from one
point like the ribs of an umbrella or parasol (to p. xix):*

64 Petals united into a short tube; Bedstraw (FIG. 62) *Galium*

64a Petals free from one another:

65 All the bunches of flower stalks (umbels) with a ring of
bracts at the base:

66 Leaves divided into 3 separate leaflets; fruits not
prickly; Clover (FIGS. 25, 26) . . *Trifolium*

66a Leaves not divided into 3 leaflets; fruits prickly:

67 Leaves divided fan-wise almost to the base; fruits with
numerous hooks; flowers in head-like clusters;
Wood Sanicle (FIG. 132) . . . . *Sanicula*

67a Leaves much divided into fine segments; fruits with
rows of prickles like a comb; Wild Carrot (FIG.
133) . . . . *Daucus*

65a Not all the bunches of flower-stalks (umbels) with a
ring of bracts at the base:

68 Ultimate bunches of flower-stalks (umbels) with bracts
at the base (to p. xix):

69 Flowers all with more or less equal-sized petals:

70 Rootstock a rather large rounded or 2-lobed tuber;
leaves much divided into fine segments; each
carpel faintly 5-ribbed; Pignut (FIG. 134)

Conopodium

70a Rootstock not tuberous:

71 Bracts inserted all to one side of the ultimate
bunches of flowers; leaves cut into fine segments (FIG. 135) . . . . . *Aethusa*

71a Bracts not all to one side of the clusters; leaves
with broad segments:

72 Carpels in fruit narrowly winged, with the 5 resin
channels (vittas) not extended to the base, only
2 showing on the reverse side; Cow Parsnip
(FIG. 136) . . . . . . *Heracleum*

xviii

72a Carpels in fruit broadly winged, with the resin channels extending to the base, the 2 on the reverse side close to the middle and reaching to the base (FIG. 137) . . .   *Angelica*

69a Outer flowers with the outer petals larger than the others; fruits smooth and narrow; Chervil (FIG. 138) . . . .   *Anthriscus*

68a Ultimate bunches (umbels) entirely without bracts at the base:

73 Ovary below the sepals and petals (ovary inferior):

74 Leaflets broad and large, in threes; Goutweed (FIG. 139) . . . .   *Aegopodium*

74a Leaflets small and not in threes; Burnet Saxifrage (FIG. 140) . . . .   *Pimpinella*

73a Ovary above the sepals and petals (ovary superior); Greater Celandine (FIG. 76) . . *Chelidonium*

63a *Flowers not arranged in umbels (as described on p. xviii):*

75 Leaves alternate on the stems or sometimes all the leaves confined to the base of the plant (all radical) (to p. xxv):

76 Female part of the flower (in the middle) composed of 2 or more carpels free from one another (to p. xx):

77 Petals not united, or sometimes absent and sepals petal-like (to p. xx):

78 Leaves without stipules:

79 Leaves very small, thick and fleshy; flowers star-like: Stonecrop (FIG. 125) . . .   *Sedum*

79a Leaves not as above:

80 Sepals coloured, but no petals:

81 Sepals yellow, like a buttercup; Marsh Marigold (FIG. 68) . . . .   *Caltha*

81a Sepals mauve or white; Wood Anemone (FIG. 72) . . . .   *Anemone*

80a Sepals green:

82 Petals 5; sepals 5; Buttercup (FIGS. 69, 70)   *Ranunculus*

82a Petals more than 5; sepals 3; Lesser Celandine (FIG. 71) . . . .   *Ficaria*

78a Leaves with stipules:

83 Carpels when ripe enclosed by the calyx-tube (receptacle), the latter furnished with hooked prickles; Common Agrimony (FIG. 18)

Agrimonia

83a Carpels when ripe not enclosed by the receptacle:
84 Calyx-lobes 5 (without a second series of smaller
sepals or bracts); Meadow-Sweet (FIG. 10)
Filipendula
84a Calyx-lobes 10 (made up of 5 sepals and 5 bracts):
85 Style elongating after flowering and becoming
hooked; leaves with large leafy stipules;
Common Avens (FIG. 17) . . . . *Geum*
85 Style not elongated after flowering, and not forming
a hook:
86 Achenes (little fruits like seeds) arranged on a
small dry receptacle (FIGS. 11, 12, 13)
Potentilla
86a Achenes (little fruits like seeds) arranged on a
fleshy enlarged receptacle; Wild Strawberry (FIG. 14) . . . . . *Fragaria*
77a Petals united into a tube; leaves orbicular, attached
in the middle like the stalk of a mushroom; Navel-
wort or Penny-wort (FIG. 126) . . *Umbilicus*
76a Female (middle) part of the flower composed of a single
ovary (i.e. made up of one carpel or 2 or more
united carpels):

87 **Petals present, free or united into a tube (to p. xxv):**
88 **Sepals and petals inserted below or around the ovary (ovary
superior) (to p. xxiv):**
89 Stamens with their stalks united into a column or
sheath (in the latter case sometimes split down
one side) (to p. xxi):
90 Flowers divisible into equal halves in only one
direction, " irregular "; mostly the Pea family
(to p. xxi):
91 Common stalk of all the flowers arranged opposite
the leaf (leaf-opposed); back petal with a
pouch at the base; Fumitory (FIG. 77) *Fumaria*
91a Common stalk or separate stalks of the flowers
not opposite the leaf:
92 Leaf-stalks ending in a tendril:
93 Wing petals adherent to the keel petals; style
thread-like throughout; Vetch (FIGS. 23, 24)
Vicia
93a Wing petals free or nearly so; style flattened,
with a longitudinal beard below the apex;
Wild Pea (FIG. 22) . . . . *Lathyrus*

92a Leaf-stalks not ending in a tendril:

94 Flowers in a head; leaflets 3:

95 Stipules unlike the leaflets; Clover (FIGS. 25, 26)
Trifolium

95a Stipules like the leaflets; Bird's Foot Trefoil
(FIG. 27) . . . . *Lotus*

94a Flowers not in a head:

96 Leaves narrow, not glandular; Milkwort (FIG.
41) . . . . *Polygala*

96a Leaves elliptic, glandular; Restharrow (FIG.
21) . . . . *Ononis*

90a Flowers divisible into equal halves in several
directions (" regular "):

97 Leaves not divided into leaflets; Dwarf Mallow
(FIG. 44) . . . . *Malva*

97a Leaves divided into 3 leaflets; Wood Sorrel
(FIG. 184) . . . . *Oxalis*

89a Stamens not united into a column or sheath; sometimes inserted on the corolla:

98 Stamens numerous (more than double the number
of the petals):

99 Sepals 5 or 4, persistent:

100 Leaves pinnate; flowers yellow, arranged in a
stiff spike; Common Agrimony (FIG. 18)
Agrimonia

100a Leaves lobed fan-wise; flowers very small,
greenish-yellow, arranged in small irregular
clusters on slender stalks; Lady's Mantle
(FIG. 15) . . . . . . *Alchemilla*

99a Sepals 2, falling off as the flowers open:

101 Ovary and fruit globular; stigmas radiating on
top of the ovary and fruit; flowers red;
Common Poppy (FIG. 74) . *Papaver*

101a Ovary and fruit linear; flowers yellow:

102 Flowers large and solitary; Sea Poppy (FIG. 75)
Glaucium

102a Flowers small, in an umbel opposite the leaf;
Greater Celandine (FIG. 76) *Chelidonium*

98a Stamens few, not more than double the number of
the petals:

103 *Petals not united into a tube (to p. xxiii):*

104 Stamens 6, 4 long and 2 shorter; petals 4;
Wall-flower family (to p. xxiii):

105 Flowers yellow or reddish:

   106 Perennials with glabrous or very shortly hairy stems:

      107 Stem-leaves eared at the base; Wintercress (FIG. 78) . . . . . *Barbarea*

      107a Stem-leaves not eared at the base; Wallflower (FIG. 82) . . . . . *Cheiranthus*

   106a Annuals with stiff whitish hairs on the stems:

      108 Fruits opening and releasing the seeds; leaves toothed or shortly lobed; Charlock (FIG. 83) . . . . . *Sinapis*

      108a Fruits not opening; leaves deeply pinnately lobed; Wild Radish (FIG. 89) *Raphanus*

105a Flowers white, pink, or mauve:

   109 Fruits at least 3 or 4 times as long as broad:

      110 Leaves at most toothed (not pinnately lobed):

         111 Leaves all stalked, large and broad, widely heart-shaped at the base; Garlic Mustard (FIG. 84) . . . *Alliaria*

         111a Leaves sessile or ear-shaped at the base, the basal leaves forming a rosette; Hairy Rockcress (FIG. 85) *Arabis*

      110a Leaves (at least the lower) pinnate (deeply divided into separate leaflets):

         112 Fruits opening and releasing the seeds, not long-beaked:

            113 Seeds arranged in two rows on each placenta and partition of the fruit; flowers white; Watercress (FIG. 79) *Nasturtium*

            113a Seeds arranged in one row; flowers often mauve (FIGS. 80, 81) *Cardamine*

         112a Fruits not opening, long-beaked; stems with stiff bristly spreading hairs (FIG. 89) . . . . . . *Raphanus*

   109a Fruits less than 3 times as long as broad:

      114 Fruits flat and orbicular, broadly winged; hairs on the leaves not star-shaped; Penny Cress (FIG. 88) . . *Thlaspi*

      114a Fruits wedge-shaped, not winged; hairs on the leaves star-shaped; Shepherd's Purse (FIG. 87) . . . . . *Capsella*

114b Fruits oblong-elliptic; hairs star-shaped
      Whitlow-grass (FIG. 86) . . *Erophila*
104a Stamens more or fewer than 6; petals usually 5:
115 Petals deeply lobed; flowers in a stiff spike-like
      raceme; Mignonette (FIG. 91) . *Reseda*
115a Petals entire or at most notched at the apex:
116 Flowers solitary:
   117 Leaves divided into 3, like Clover; petals
         not spurred; Wood Sorrel (FIG. 184)
                                          Oxalis
   117a Leaves not divided into leaflets; lower petal
         spurred; Violet (FIGS. 39, 40) . *Viola*
116a Flowers not solitary:
   118 Leaves pinnate; flowers crimson, in a dense
         head; Greater Salad Burnet (FIG. 16)
                                       Sanguisorba
   118a Leaves lobed fan-wise; flowers in small
         loose clusters; Lady's Mantle (FIG. 15)
                                       Alchemilla
103a *Petals united into a tube:*
119 Stamens placed opposite to the corolla-lobes and
      equal to them in number; Primrose and
      Cowslip (FIGS. 121, 122) . . *Primula*
119a Stamens placed between the corolla-lobes,
      sometimes fewer in number:
120 Ovary deeply and vertically lobed, with the
      style inserted between the lobes:
   121 Lobes of the corolla spreading horizontally;.
         corolla with a distinct "eye" around the
         almost closed tube:
      122 Flowers arranged on one side of the axis, the
            latter coiled in bud; Forget-me-not (FIG.
            186) . . . . *Myosotis*
      122a Flowers not arranged as above, more or
            less solitary; Evergreen Alkanet (FIG.
            185) . . . . *Anchusa*
   121a Lobes of the corolla not spreading horizont-
         ally; corolla with an open tube and no
         "eye"; Comfrey (FIG. 187) *Symphytum*
120a Ovary not vertically lobed; style terminal:
123 Corolla spurred at the base, 2-lipped; leaves
      small and rounded, coarsely toothed;
      Ivy-leaved Toadflax (FIG. 181) *Linaria*

123a Corolla not spurred at the base and not 2-lipped:

124 Flowers numerous in a long erect spike-like inflorescence:

125 Flowers pendulous and to one side of the spike; corolla long and tubular, mostly spotted inside; Foxglove (FIG. 178) . . . . *Digitalis*

125a Flowers not pendulous; tube short, not spotted; Mullein (FIG. 177)

Verbascum

124a Flowers not arranged as above, solitary or few together:

126 Anthers opening by a hole (pore) at the top; Black Nightshade and Bittersweet (FIGS. 171, 172) . . *Solanum*

126a Anthers opening by a slit lengthwise:

127 Aquatic plant: leaves divided into 3 leaflets; Buckbean (FIG. 118) *Menyanthes*

127a Not aquatics; leaves not as above:

128 Perennial, twining or creeping plants; leaves not lobed, except at the base; seeds few:

129 Bracts small, at a distance from the calyx; stigmas narrow; Lesser Bindweed (FIG. 175) *Convolvulus*

129a Bracts large, close under the calyx; stigmas broad; Large Bindweed (FIG. 176) . . . . *Calystegia*

128a Annual plant, not twining or creeping:

130 Leaves coarsely lobed; seeds very numerous; Henbane (FIG. 174)

Hyoscyamus

130a Leaves entire, in unequal-sized pairs; Deadly Nightshade (FIG. 173)

Atropa

88a *Sepals and petals inserted above the ovary* (*ovary inferior*):

131 Leaves attached to the middle of the orbicular blade, like the stalk of a mushroom; Marsh Pennywort (FIG. 131). . . . *Hydrocotyle*

131a Leaves attached at the base:

132 Petals free from one another:

133 Stamens 10; hairs on the stem tipped with a
gland; Meadow Saxifrage (FIG. 127)

Saxifraga

133a Stamens 8; hairs not gland-tipped; Rose-bay
and Great Willow-herb (FIGS. 108, 109)

Epilobium

132a Petals united into a tube:

134 Small herb, not climbing; flowers blue or white,
bisexual; Harebell (FIG. 141)   *Campanula*

134a Climber with tendrils; flowers small, yellowish-
green, unisexual; Bryony (FIG. 42) *Bryonia*

87a **Petals absent:**

135 Leaves with large sheathing stipules:

136 Flowers in slender panicles; leaves arrow-shaped
at the base; Sheep Sorrel (FIG. 112)   *Rumex*

136a Flowers in heads; leaves pinnate; Greater Salad
Burnet (FIG. 16)   .   .   .   .   *Sanguisorba*

136b Flowers in small axillary clusters; leaves narrow
at the base; Knotweed (FIG. 111)

Polygonum

135a Leaves without stipules:

137 Plants without milky juice:

138 Calyx or bracts enlarged in fruit; lower leaves
mostly opposite, more or less triangular with
2 spreading lobes near the base; Common
Orache (FIG. 114)   .   .   .   .   .   *Atriplex*

138a Calyx not enlarged in fruit or only slightly so:

139 Leaves at most bluntly and coarsely toothed,
more or less triangular or rhomboid; White
Goosefoot (FIG. 113)   .   .   *Chenopodium*

139a Leaves entire; flowers in axillary clusters; Wall
Pellitory (FIG. 36)   .   .   .   .   *Parietaria*

139b Leaves deeply pinnate; inflorescence opposite
the leaf (FIG. 90)   .   .   .   .   *Coronopus*

137a Plants with milky juice; leaves entire; Spurges
(FIGS. 47, 48)   .   .   .   .   .   .   *Euphorbia*

75a **Leaves opposite or in whorls on the stem, not all at the base
of the plant:**

140 Water plant with submerged deeply divided whorled
leaves with very narrow divisions; Water-Milfoil
(FIG. 105)   .   .   .   .   *Myriophyllum*

140a Not as above:

141 Petals absent:

xxvi

156 Ovary above the sepals and petals (not united
 with the calyx):
157 Styles 5:
 158 Ovary and fruit divided into separate compartments; delicate glabrous annual
  plant; Purging Flax (FIG. 45) . *Linum*
 158a Ovary and fruit not divided into compartments:
  159 Hairy plants:
   160 Fruit opening by 10 small teeth at the top;
    Mouse-ear Chickweed (FIG. 94)
               Cerastium
   160a Fruit opening by 5 teeth; flowers showy,
    Corncockle (FIG. 101) . *Lychnis*
  159a Glabrous plants; fruit splitting low down
    into 4 or 5 valves; Pearlworts (FIGS.
    95, 96) . . . . *Sagina*
157a Styles 3; fruit opening at the top by 6 small
  teeth; Sandwort (FIGS. 97, 98) *Arenaria*
157b Style 1:
 161 Creeping plant with minute flowers in the
  axils of the leaves; Water Purslane (FIG.
  106) . . . . *Peplis*
 161a Erect plants with showy flowers; Purple
  Loosestrife (FIG. 107) . . *Lythrum*
156a Ovary below the sepals and petals (ovary
  inferior), and united with sepals:
 162 Petals 4; stamens 8; fruits without hooks;
  Rosebay and Willow-herb (FIGS. 108, 109)
             Epilobium
 162a Petals 2; stamens 2; fruits covered with
  hooked bristles; Enchanter's Nightshade
  (FIG. 110)   *Circaea*

146a *Petals united into a tube:*
 163 Stamens opposite to the corolla-lobes, equal in
  number to the latter:
  164 Tall erect plants up to about 3 ft., with panicles of
   yellow flowers; Yellow Loosestrife (FIG. 119)
            Lysimachia
  164a Procumbent small annual, with usually red
   flowers; Scarlet Pimpernel (FIG. 120) *Anagallis*
 163a Stamens alternate with the corolla-lobes, sometimes fewer in number:

165 *Ovary inserted above the calyx and corolla (ovary superior) (to p. xxix)* :

166 Stamens 2; flowers blue, with a white " eye ";
    Germander Speedwell (FIG. 179)   *Veronica*

166a Stamens more than 2:

  167 Style placed on top of the ovary, the latter not deeply vertically divided:

    168 Flowers regular, i.e. divisible into equal halves in several directions:

      169 Small herbs; with small equal-sized leaves:

        170 Flowers pale blue; calyx not divided to the base; Gentian (FIGS. 115, 116) *Gentiana*

        170a Flowers pink or reddish; calyx divided to the base; Centaury (FIG. 117)

                      Centaurium

      169a Large much-branched herbs, with unequal-sized leaves in pairs on one side of the stem; fruit a black berry; Deadly Nightshade (FIG. 173)   *Atropa*

    168a Flowers irregular, i.e. divisible into equal halves in only one (vertical) direction, usually more or less 2-lipped; very small annuals; Eyebright (FIG. 180) *Euphrasia*

  167a Style placed between the lobes of the deeply (vertically) divided ovary, the latter with 4 rounded lobes:

    171 Flowers yellow, all turned towards one side of the axis; leaves markedly wrinkled-reticulate; Woodsage (FIG. 189)

                      Teucrium

    171a Flowers not yellow, arranged in axillary clusters or whorls more or less all around the axis or stem:

      172 Calyx-lobes long and spine-like, much longer than the tube; corolla-tube very hairy outside, 2-lipped; annual plants; Hemp-nettle (FIG. 193) . . . *Galeopsis*

      172a Calyx-lobes not as above, at most only slightly longer than the tube:

        173 Corolla almost regular (neither 1-lipped nor 2-lipped); flowers pink in a rounded cluster at the top of the shoots; Water-mint (FIG. 188) . . . . *Mentha*

173a Corolla very irregular, either 1-lipped or
    2-lipped:
174 Corolla with an upper and lower lip:
175 Leaves fairly large and usually toothed;
    plants not forming carpets as described
    below:
176 Rather tall plant (up to 4 ft. high);
    anthers not hairy (FIG. 190) *Stachys*
176a Dwarfer plants:
177 Anthers hairy; nutlets flat on top;
    Dead-nettle (FIG. 191) .   *Lamium*
177a Anthers not hairy; nutlets not flat on
    top:
178 Calyx-lobes equal-sized or nearly so;
    Ground Ivy (FIG. 194)   *Nepeta*
178a Calyx-lobes very unequal, the upper
    lip flat and broad; Self-heal
    (FIG. 195) . . . . *Prunella*
175a Leaves very small and entire; low de-
    cumbent plant often forming a con-
    tinuous flat carpet; Wild Thyme
    (FIG. 192) . . . . . *Thymus*
174a Corolla without an upper lip; creeping
    plant; flowers in the axils of nearly
    all the leaves; Common Bugle (FIG.
    196) . . . . *Ajuga*

165a *Ovary below the calyx and corolla (ovary inferior):*
179 Stamens 4; leaves in whorls:
180 Corolla with tube as long as the lobes; grows
    in woods in shade of trees; Woodruff (FIG.
    63) . . . . *Asperula*
180a Corolla with a very short tube; not in shade
    (FIGS. 61, 62)   . . . . *Galium*
179a Stamens 3; leaves in pairs; Cornsalad (FIG. 130)
    Valerianella

Key, Part III.

1 Not grasses or sedges or in any way like them:
2 Flowers arranged on a spadix surrounded by a spathe;
  Lords and Ladies (FIG. 200) . . . . . . *Arum*
2a Flowers not arranged as above:
3 Ovary above the petals (perianth):

4 Flowers in a large panicle, rather small (FIG. 197)

Alisma

    4a Flowers not in a panicle:

       5 Flowers white in an umbel surrounded by bracts;
          Wild Onion (FIG. 199) . . .   *Allium*

       5a Flowers usually blue, not in an umbel; Bluebell (FIG.
          198) . . . .   *Scilla*

    3a Ovary below the petals (perianth); flowers large, yellow
      with large petal-like stigmas; Yellow Flag (FIG. 201)

Iris

1a Grass or Sedge-like plants (FIG. 202) . . . . .   *Luzula*

1. Yew, *Taxus baccata* L. (A, male shoot, × ⅔; B, shoot with
"fruit," × ⅔); small tree often used as a garden hedge and in
topiary work; "flowers" very inconspicuous, the males
(A1, × 1¼) on one tree, the females (C, × 2) on another (dioecious); the pollen from the male is blown by the wind to the
female, the latter consisting of an exposed ovule on a short
shoot of its own and surrounded by small overlapping scales
(C, × 2); unlike other conifers, Yew trees have no cones, and so
there is no real fruit; but the seed (D, E, × 1¼) is surrounded by
a red sweet fleshy cup-like structure (aril) which is a great attrac-

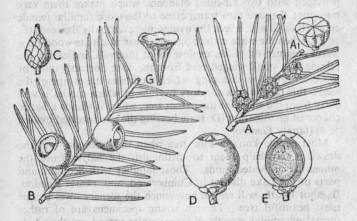

tion to birds, who pass the seed without injury, for the seed
itself is very poisonous; it is thus distributed away from the
parent tree (G, ripe male scale, × 2½) (family *Taxaceae*).

The Yew is very widely spread in most parts of Europe, from
Britain and Scandinavia to western Russia, and from Algeria to
as far east as Burma and even the Philippines. The further
south it occurs, the higher it ascends the mountains, for example
up to 5400 ft. in the Pyrenees.

One can nearly always find a Yew in a country churchyard.
It was of value in olden times for making bows. In this country
it is best seen as a wild tree in the chalk downs of southern
England. Yews live to a great age, up to about 3000 years, the
highest recorded being about 30 ft., with a trunk 12 ft. in diameter.
The wood throws out a great heat when burned.

2. Scots Fir, Scots Pine, *Pinus sylvestris* L. ($\times \frac{2}{5}$); branches of two kinds, long and short shoots, the former growing on without interruption each year, the latter bearing the pair of needle-like leaves which arise in the midst of small scales; after persisting for three or four years these leaf-bearing short shoots fall off, and are really deciduous (term for leaves falling off), though the tree is of course always green (evergreen); the male or staminate "cones" are crowded towards the top of the shoot (A), and about the end of May when the branches are disturbed by the wind clouds of pollen are dispersed; the pollen-grains are provided with two air-filled bladders, which makes them very buoyant; they are thus transported to the more familiar female cones (B & C) which bear the ovules and eventually the seeds (E, $\times 2$); when these are mature one may hear in a pine wood on a warm summer day little explosions at intervals, indicating the release of a small winged seed from the cone, formerly more or less erect, but now drooping, which facilitates the escape of the seed; this falls with a rotatory movement which carries it well away from the shade of the parent tree, where it stands a better chance of germination (D, scale bearing the two inverted ovules, $\times 4$) (family *Pinaceae*).

Most people know a Pine tree when they see one, and the drawing may help them to distinguish the native from the numerous cultivated kinds. Those familiar with Scotland and parts of the Lake district in Cumberland, and, nearer London, Bagshot Heath, will realise how much the scenery owes to this most beautiful tree. Though young specimens are of rather formal pyramidal growth, older examples spread out their tops like a Cedar of Lebanon, and rarely clash with other types of vegetation. Usually the Pine is associated with Heather, Ling, and Bracken.

Scots Pine is greatly valued for its timber and as firewood. Like all Conifers, it is a "softwood," as compared with Oak, a "hardwood." One can travel far abroad and still meet with the tree, sometimes in most diverse climates, even as far as Eastern Siberia, where the temperature in winter falls to $-40°$ F., and in Southern Spain, with a summer temperature up to 95° F. There are several varieties, some of which, however, are not at all constant and are dependent on soil conditions. For example, Pines which have been small and stunted assume the ordinary tall form when the condition of the soil is changed by draining.

3. Juniper, *Juniperus communis* L.; evergreen shrub, much branched, with very sharp prickly short narrow evergreen leaves, these in whorls of 3 and glaucous above; male and female cones usually on different plants (dioecious), axillary, very small, the male (C, × 2) consisting of several broad shortly pointed scales (D, × 3) each with about 4 anther-loculi attached to the lower margin, the female with a few empty scales at the base and 3 fleshy ones above which unite to form the depressed globose cone ("fruit") (E, × 1½), which is dark purple-blue and about ⅓ in. in diam.; seeds hard; very widely distributed in North Temperate regions from the Mediterranean to the Arctic and across Asia into North America; (A, male shoot, ×⅖; B, female shoot, × ⅖); usually grows on open downs and hillsides and is locally common; a second species is *J. sibirica* Burgsd. (*J. nana* Willd.), very dwarf and in these islands found only in Scotland and the western half of Eire.

Oil of Juniper is obtained from the dried ripe female cones ("fruits"), and is colourless or pale greenish-yellow, with a characteristic odour and a burning somewhat bitter taste. It is used medicinally, and the berries are also employed for flavouring gin (family *Cupressaceae*).

4. Sloe, *Prunus spinosa* L. ($\times \frac{2}{5}$); flowers appearing before the leaves on short lateral spine-tipped branchlets; calyx (A, nat. size) with 5 lanceolate lobes, lined inside with a 10-lobed disk; petals (B, $\times 2\frac{1}{4}$) white; stamens about 12–15, the yellow anthers attached at the back above the base (C, $\times 6$); carpel (D, $\times 2$) 1, free within the calyx-tube, gradually narrowed into a rather long slender style tipped with a head-like (capitate) stigma; largest leaves (E, $\times \frac{2}{5}$) on the longer shoots which bear neither flowers nor fruit, more or less elliptic and rather shortly toothed; fruits (F, $\times \frac{2}{5}$) blue-black and globular or broadly elliptic (family *Rosaceae*).

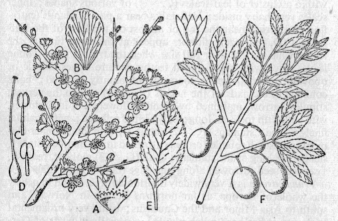

The fruit of the Sloe, like that of the cherry (fig. 5), is known as a drupe or stone fruit, in which the outer part is fleshy, and the inner part is hard and stony and contains a single seed; it is very astringent, but makes a fairly good jam; formerly used in making British "Port Wine," and the juice for marking-ink; wood tough and used as teeth for rakes. The spine-tipped branchlets protect the young foliage from browsing animals and the plant is useful for hedges. Damsons and the various kinds of Plums of our gardens are derived from forms of the Sloe. It is not likely to be confused with other wild species of the genus, *Prunus avium* L. (see fig. 5), and *P. padus* L., the Bird Cherry, or Hackberry, as it is often called in the north; the latter has rather long racemes of small white flowers and black very bitter shining fruits.

5. Wild Cherry or Gean, *Prunus avium* L. ($\times \frac{1}{3}$); in woods
and hedges, and generally distributed; common in beechwoods;
sometimes nearly 100 ft. high, with a girth up to 12 ft.; trunk
often unbranched to a considerable height, and covered with a
thin smooth greyish bark which peels off in transverse strips;
branches long and spreading, of two kinds, long shoots (A, $\times \frac{1}{3}$),
and very short shoots (B, $\times \frac{1}{3}$), the long shoots continuing to
elongate, the short shoots bearing an annual crop of flowers and,
or, leaves; long shoots smooth between the short shoots, and
tinged with purple; short shoots scarred by the stalks of the
leaves of previous years; current season's leaves produced from
within a cluster of leaf-scales (C, $\times \frac{1}{2}$) of various shapes; inner
scales very hairy inside; leaf-stalks bear a pair of glands (extrafloral nectaries) near the top or almost on the base of the leaf-
margin (D, nat. size); flowers appear at the same time as the
leaves which attain their full size when the fruit is ripe; young
leaves often with gland-tipped teeth; mature leaves elliptic or
obovate, pointed, rather coarsely but bluntly toothed; hairs
confined to the axils of the nerves (E, $\times 2\frac{1}{2}$) and to the nerves;
stipules narrow, margined by glands; flowers 2–6 in a cluster,
with stalks up to $1\frac{1}{2}$ in. long; calyx-lobes reflexed; petals white,
finely veined; stamens (F, $\times 2$) about 25, with long slender filaments and small rounded anthers attached in the middle; style 1,
slender, as long as the stamens; fruit (G, $\times \frac{3}{4}$) globose, reddish,
1-seeded, seed furrowed along one edge (family *Rosaceae*).

Prunus avium is a very widely distributed tree, found in nearly
the whole of Europe, as far north as Bergen in Norway, and
south to Asia Minor and the Caucasus; being very ornamental
in flower, it has been much planted, especially in parts of Ger-
many, where it is grown alongside the highways. It is considered to be a native of the southern counties of England. In
Scotland it is usually called Gean. The wood is scarce, but is
one of the best native timbers for inside work, possessing a fine
even grain and taking a good surface and polish. It is likely to
be confused with only one other native species, *P. cerasus* L.,
which, however, never becomes a tree, but remains a bushy shrub
with much-branched stems, and from the roots are produced
numerous suckers.

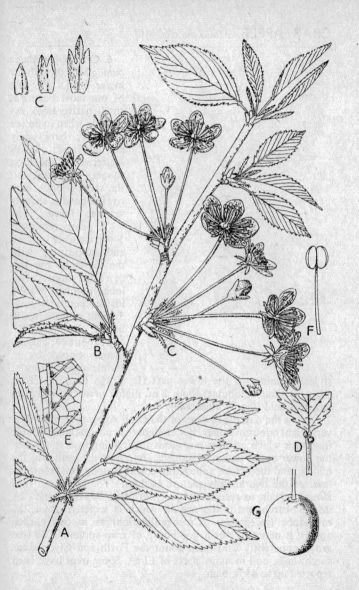

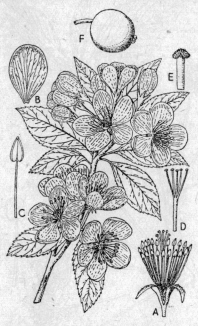

6. Crab Apple, *Malus pumila* Mill. (syn. *Pyrus malus* L.) (× $\frac{2}{5}$); one of our most beautiful small native trees, especially when in flower or fruit; bark scaly and fissured; leaves scattered on the long shoots, clustered on the short shoots, narrowly obovate, sharply serrate; flowers (A, × $\frac{4}{5}$, petals removed) 5–6 in a cluster (umbel) and appearing with the leaves at the top of a short shoot; calyx-lobes pointed, woolly inside; petals (B, × $\frac{4}{5}$) 5, pink outside, white inside; stamens (C, × 2) about 20; anthers ovate, tipped by a gland; ovary inferior; styles 5, united in the lower part (D, × $1\frac{1}{4}$; E, × $3\frac{1}{4}$); fruit (F, × $\frac{2}{5}$) almost globular, about 1 in. diam., green flushed with red, very acid (family *Rosaceae*).

During the day the flowers of the Crab Apple give off only a very slight odour of honey, but at night they possess an agreeable fragrance which attracts numerous night-flying insects. When the flower opens the erect stamens are crowded together in the middle, and their close, yellow anthers are usually well below the level of the five already mature stigmas. The latter are thus almost certain to receive pollen from other flowers carried by insects searching for the nectar, which is secreted inside the calyx-tube (receptacle). Cross-pollination, as in our garden apples, is necessary for a good crop of crab-apples. The tree grows apparently wild from about the Forth and Clyde areas southwards, and in many parts of Eire. Some trees have been reported up to 45 ft. high.

7. Hawthorn, *Crataegus monogyna* Jacq. ($\times \frac{2}{5}$); a shrub or small tree, the branchlets often ending in stiff sharp thorns; leaves borne on very short annual shoots, stalked, with a pair of lanceolate acute leafy stipules at the base of the stalk (A, $\times 1\frac{1}{2}$); blade obovate-wedge-shaped in outline, 3-lobed, lobes ascending coarsely 2-3-toothed, bright green and glabrous or slightly hairy below in the axils of the main nerves; flowers (B, $\times 2\frac{1}{2}$) fragrant, arranged in short broad corymbs at the ends of the short leafy shoots; bracts very small and soon falling off; stalks hairy

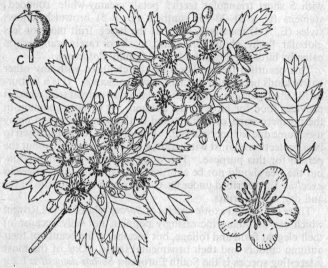

towards the top and on the calyx-tube; calyx-lobes 5, widely separated, oblong-lanceolate, not hairy; petals 5, white or tinged with pink, much overlapping in bud (imbricate), free from one another, rounded-obovate; stamens about 25; anthers pink; ovary inferior, with 1 rather thick style woolly at the base and a head-like stigma; fruit (C, $\times 1\frac{3}{4}$) a red " berry," more or less globose, crowned by the short calyx-lobes, with a mealy exterior and containing a hard nut (drupe) containing a single seed (family *Rosaceae*).

There are two species in Britain, that described above and *Crataegus oxyacanthoides* Thuill. with less cut leaves.

8. Rowan (Mountain Ash), *Sorbus aucuparia* L. ($\times \frac{1}{2}$); an elegant tree up to about 30 ft. high with numerous spreading branches; bark brownish-grey, smooth, branchlets reddish-brown; winter-buds ovoid, hairy; leaves alternate, pinnate, with about 6–8 pairs of leaflets and an end one, and a slightly winged common stalk; leaflets oblong, toothed (dentate), smooth or more or less hairy below; stipules very small and soon falling off and leaving a slight scar; flowers (B, $\times$ 4) small, rather densely arranged in a more or less flat cluster (corymb), scented; calyx (A, $\times$ 4) adnate to the lower part of the carpels, with 5 short triangular teeth; petals creamy-white, rounded; stamens (C, $\times$ 3) 20–25; anthers (D, $\times$ 5) brownish-yellow; styles (E, $\times$ 4) usually 3, hairy at the base; fruit more or less globular, fleshy, about $\frac{1}{3}$ in. diam., scarlet or rarely orange, soon eaten by birds (F, flower bud, $\times$ 4) (family *Rosaceae*).

This beautiful tree will scarcely be confused with any other native kinds because of its distinctive characters. It is a favourite for small gardens, and is often planted as a street tree, where it provides food for birds in the autumn. It is more common in the northern parts of Britain, and in the past was put to many uses, some due to superstitition. For instance, it was supposed to be a protection against witchcraft, a twig being carried about the person for this purpose. The wood is hard with a fine grain, but the tree should not be confused with the true Ash, *Fraxinus excelsior* L., described under fig. 60 and which has opposite leaves and dry winged fruits.

There are several exotic species of *Sorbus* related to the Rowan which are becoming increasingly popular, not only because of their elegant form and foliage, but because of the beauty of their autumn colours and their ornamental fruits. One of the most interesting species is the South European *Sorbus domestica* L., a single tree of which grew in the middle of the Wyre forest in Worcestershire, where is was probably introduced in Roman times. It was regarded as an old tree in 1678, and lasted until 1862, when it was maliciously burnt down. It is pleasant to recall that descendants of this tree, which was known to everyone and venerated in the neighbourhood, are still growing in the forest. The fruits are interesting, being of two shapes, on one tree being shaped like a pear, and on another like an apple.

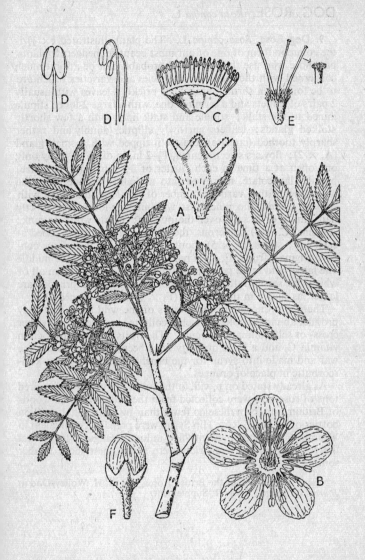

9. Dog Rose, *Rosa canina* L. The plant illustrated ($\times \frac{1}{2}$) is the common form of one of our most beautiful hedgerow plants, but those who use this book will probably not be at first much concerned with the many other species and varieties which are to be found;* a shrub; branchlets prickly; leaves with usually 2 pairs of leaflets and a terminal one, with a large 2-lobed stipule joined to the stalk; stipule and stalk lined with a few shortly stalked glands; leaflets narrowly elliptic, doubly and rather sharply toothed (crenate), the teeth tipped with a small gland (A, $\times$ 2); flowers sweet-scented, $1\frac{1}{2}$–2 in. in diam., usually only one open at a time in each cluster of 3; sepals (B, nat. size) broadly lanceolate, narrowed into a slightly broader top, the outer ones with a variable number of side-lobes margined with stalked glands, the innermost without side-lobes and shortly hairy more or less all over the outside; petals white or pink; stamens (C, $\times$ 3) numerous, the anthers rather deeply lobed at each end; styles (D, $\times$ 5) about 25, hairy, with an oblique concave stigma; fruits (E, $\times \frac{3}{4}$) red, usually 3 together, the middle one larger and more pear-shaped than the side ones, from all of which the sepals fall off; in vigorous shoots the prickles are larger, as shown in the drawing (F, $\times \frac{3}{4}$) (family *Rosaceae*).

There is no nectar in the flowers of the wild roses, but they produce abundant pollen, which is collected by insects, and either cross- or self-pollination occurs. The fruits of many are rich in vitamin C, and a large quantity have been gathered during the war and made into syrup for the benefit of children as an antiscorbutic in place of oranges.

As already stated on p. viii, in the year 1943 over five hundred tons of rose-hips were collected from the hedgerows and woods of Britain, and from these no fewer than two and a half million bottles of National Rose Hip Syrup were prepared, equivalent in Vitamin C content to twenty-five million oranges. In general the roses in northern districts were richer than those further south.

* See "A Revision of the British Roses," by A. H. Wolley-Dod in *Journal of Botany*, 1930–31, Supplement.

10. Meadow-Sweet, *Filipendula ulmaria* (L.) Maxim. ($\times \frac{2}{5}$); rootstock short and creeping; stem purplish, up to 4 ft. high; basal leaves (A, $\times \frac{2}{5}$) large, pinnate; terminal leaflets deeply 3-4-lobed; lateral leaflets more or less elliptic, doubly and finely toothed (serrulate); between the larger leaflets are pairs of small leaflets; all with a dense felt of white hairs or sometimes almost without hairs below; stipules leafy, ear-shaped; upper stem-leaves smaller and usually only 3-lobed; flowers (B, $\times 2$) arranged in a cyme with the lateral branches longer than those in the middle, $\frac{1}{4}$-in. diam.; calyx-lobes ovate, reflexed; petals (C, $\times 3$) creamy-white, clawed; stamens (D, $\times 12$) numerous;

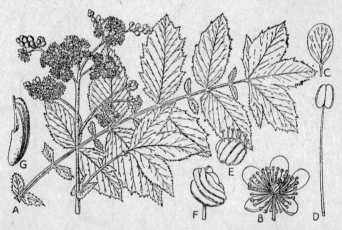

carpels (E, $\times 4$) free, and with short subterminal styles and head-like (capitate) stigmas, becoming more twisted and falcate in fruit (F, $\times 1\frac{1}{2}$) (G, $\times 2\frac{1}{2}$) (family *Rosaceae*).

This is one of our most attractive wild plants, generally distributed in wet meadows and near water; it will not always be found in botanical books under the genus name *Filipendula*, but often as *Spiraea*. The genus *Astilbe* (family *Saxifragaceae*), a common greenhouse pot plant, is often called by gardeners *Spiraea*. True Spiraeas, however, are woody, and our plant is sufficiently distinct to bear a different generic name. Botanists do not always agree about points such as these, though there is not much difference of opinion regarding the genera of our common plants.

11. **Creeping Cinquefoil,** *Potentilla reptans* L. ($\times \frac{1}{2}$); perennial herb with a slender rootstock and slender creeping stems which root at the nodes and form new plants; leaves on long slender stalks, divided fan-wise into 5 separate leaflets, the latter oblanceolate and rather coarsely toothed; stipules ovate, large, not divided; flowers $\frac{3}{4}$–1 in. across, on slender stalks (pedicels) usually longer than the leaves; calyx with 5 ovate-triangular lobes and narrower lobes (bractlets) between (A, $\times \frac{3}{5}$); petals (B, $\times 1\frac{1}{2}$) bright yellow, widely notched at the top; stamens about 20; anthers (C, $\times$ 5) egg-shaped (ovoid), opening at the

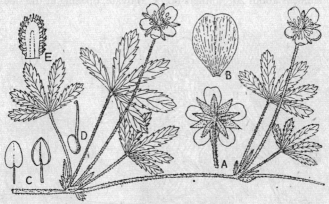

sides; achenes (D, $\times$ 8) numerous, inserted on a hairy conical axis (E, $\times$ 2), with the slender style inserted on one side and crowned by a small head-like (capitate) stigma (family *Rosaceae*).

This is a very common species in meadows and by roadsides mixed with other " herbage," and it flowers during summer and autumn. It becomes rather scarce north of the Forth and Clyde. Besides the two other common species of the genus illustrated (figures 12 and 13), only one other is common and liable to be mistaken for *P. reptans*. This is *P. tormentilla* Sibth., which has only 4 petals in all or nearly all the flowers, and the upper leaves are not stalked.

As in other species of the genus, the nectar is secreted in the form of a shining layer on the inner wall of the calyx-tube or receptacle around the base of the stamens. Cross-pollination is usually effected by insect-visitors, but automatic self-pollination also takes place owing to the closing of the flowers in dull weather and during the night.

12. Silver Weed, *Potentilla anserina* L. ($\times \frac{2}{5}$); perennial with slender rootstock, giving off procumbent runners; leaves all radical, more or less horizontally spreading, silky and silvery-white on both sides; leaflets up to about 15 pairs, sessile, oblanceolate, sharply toothed, with smaller pairs of leaflets between; flowers about 1 in. diam., solitary on slender stalks from the rootstock or in the leaf-axils on the runners; sepals and bracts of the epicalyx together 10, almost equal, but in two distinct whorls, hairy (see fig. A, flower from below, $\times \frac{2}{3}$); petals (B, nat. size) yellow, finely veined, almost orbicular; stamens about 20; anthers (C, $\times 3$) ovate, opening at the side;

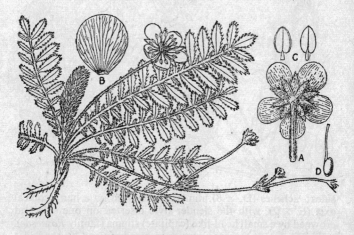

carpels (D, $\times 2$) numerous, elliptic, with the slender style inserted towards the top (family *Rosaceae*).

If South Africa has its Silver tree, we have a similarly coloured weed, for it is silky and silvery-white all over; it grows in damp meadows and banks of ditches as well as damp places on road-sides. In this species the nectar is secreted as a thin shining film on the inner wall of the calyx-tube around the base of the stamens, and is of a dark or reddish-yellow colour. If insect-visitors alight in the middle of the flower they effect cross-pollination, but if this does not occur automatic self-pollination takes place on account of the flowers closing up completely at night or in dull weather.

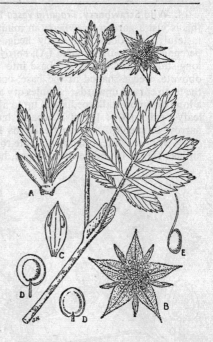

13. Marsh Cinquefoil, *Potentilla palustris* (L.) Scop. ($\times \frac{2}{5}$); in marshy places and spongy peat-bogs, especially in hilly districts; whole plant strongly astringent; rootstock blackish, creeping in the mud; lower leaves stalked, with a terminal and 2–3 pairs of lateral leaflets; stalk hairy, with the large stipule joined to it for some distance from its base; leaflets elliptic, very coarsely toothed (serrate); upper leaves (A, $\times \frac{1}{2}$) much smaller and very shortly stalked, with only 3 leaflets, and with a pair of large ear-like stipules at the base; flowers (B, $\times \frac{1}{2}$) dark-purple, up to $1\frac{1}{2}$ in. diam., very few in a terminal leafy cluster, stalked; calyx-lobes 5, broad and sharply pointed, alternating with much smaller bractlets (*epicalyx*), opposite which are the quite small petals (C, $\times 2\frac{1}{2}$); stamens 20–25, inserted on a broad flat hairy disk; anthers (D, $\times 5$) purple, almost orbicular, opening at the side; carpels (E, $\times 3$) numerous, with the slender style arising from near the base; roots formerly used in tanning; they yield a yellowish dye (family *Rosaceae*).

In the case of this flower the duty of attracting insects has been largely assumed by the calyx, which is dark purple in the lower part, the petals being quite small and not at all conspicuous. The stamens are in two whorls and at first erect over the stigmas. But the latter are not mature and receptive until after the anthers have opened and shed their pollen. Afterwards the filaments bend outwards, leaving the space they occupied in the middle of the flower free for the styles to receive pollen carried from another flower by insects collecting the nectar secreted in the large disk.

14. Wild Strawberry, *Fragaria vesca* L. ($\times \frac{1}{2}$); in appearance this is just a garden strawberry in miniature, and sometimes as tasteful; in woods and shady hedge-banks, often plentiful; perennial herb with runners (A), softly hairy all over; leaves long-stalked, divided to the base into three leaflets, the latter obovate, wedge-shaped at the base, coarsely toothed (serrate), the teeth curved upwards; stipules dry and thin; flowers few on a long common stalk (peduncle) up to about a foot long; bracts leafy; calyx (B, $\times 1\frac{1}{2}$) of 5 broadly lanceolate lobes and with narrow bracteoles between nearly as long, pubescent; petals (C, $\times 3$) pure white, broadly obovate-rounded; stamens 15–20; anthers (D, $\times 10$) horse-shoe shaped, heart-shaped at the base,

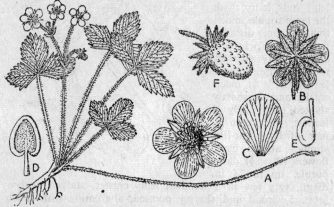

opening at the sides; carpels (E, $\times 10$) free, crowded in the middle of the flower and inserted on a conical axis, quite smooth (glabrous), with the short style inserted on one side; the fruit (F, $\times 1\frac{1}{2}$) axis enlarges and becomes either globular or egg-shaped (ovoid), juicy and sweet and bears the small ripe fruitlets (achenes) on the outside (family *Rosaceae*).

This wild plant is the parent of all our cultivated varieties of Alpine strawberries, and propagates itself by means of runners on which buds arise at the nodes as well as at the tip. These develop into new plants after the connecting portions have died away. Suppose a strawberry plant sends out three runners during a season, each takes root at five nodes, and from every node a new plant develops, so that the following year the mother plant is surrounded by fifteen offspring!

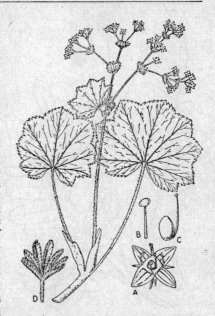

15. Lady's Mantle, *Alchemilla vulgaris* L., (aggregate) ($\times \frac{2}{5}$); perennial herb; rootstock thick; basal leaves on long stalks, kidney-shaped in outline, heart-shaped at the base, shortly and broadly 5–7-lobed, margin sharply toothed; main nerves as many as lobes, radiating fan-wise from the top of the stalk, not hairy below; upper stem-leaves becoming much smaller and less stalked, with a pair of coarsely toothed stipules like small leaves; flowers (A, $\times 4\frac{1}{2}$) greenish-yellow, arranged in small irregular clusters on slender stalks, with leafy bracts; sepals 4, with alternate smaller ones (bracts), green, 3-nerved; petals none; stamens (B, $\times 8$) 4, alternating with the larger sepals and opposite the small sepals (really small bracteoles forming an *epicalyx*); ovary (C, $\times 6$) composed of one carpel in the middle of a large fleshy disk, with the slender style arising from the base, and with a head-like stigma (family *Rosaceae*).

The roots taste like parsnip and are much sought after by pigs. It flowers from spring to autumn, in pastures and by streams. The popular name refers to the shape of leaves resembling a lady's mantle of olden times. If the young leaves be examined in bud it will be found that they are plaited and folded like a fan (D, $\times \frac{2}{5}$), and the green parts between the main radiating nerves are deeply folded and closely packed. The flowers vary a good deal in their structure and tend to become unisexual; in some the stamens are developed and the style is very short, or the stamens are vestigial or partly so and the style is well developed.

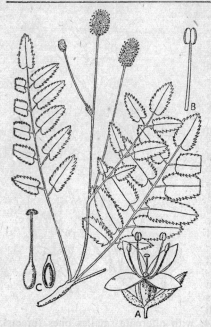

16. Greater Salad Burnet, *Sanguisorba officinalis* L. ($\times \frac{1}{2}$); perennial herb with a woody rootstock and annual stems up to about 2 ft. high; leaves mostly basal and from the lower part of the stem, pinnate with opposite stalked broadly oblong coarsely toothed (dentate) glabrous leaflets; upper part of stem branched into rather long peduncles each bearing an oblong-cylindric head of dark crimson or purple flowers (A, $\times$ 4); calyx-tube enclosed in 2–4 bracts, 4-ribbed, the 4 lobes coloured like petals; no petals; stamens (B, $\times$ 4) 4, opposite the lobes; globular disk around the style at the base of the calyx-lobes; ovary (C, $\times$ 5) embraced by the calyx-tube but quite free from it, 1-locular, with 1 ovule; style slender, with a very large disk-like papillous stigma; fruit dry, enclosed by the persistent ribbed calyx-tube; grows in moist meadows, mainly in northern Britain (family *Rosaceae*).

Surrounding the base of the style is a nectar-secreting ring, and the four calyx-lobes act as nectar receptacles. A striking feature of the flower-head is that the flowers open in succession from below upwards, so that only a zone one flower deep is in bloom at the same time. Insect visitors effect cross-pollination, though self-pollination may also take place automatically.

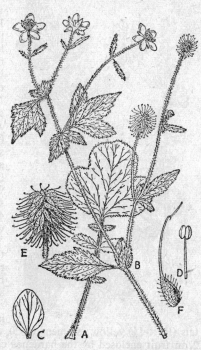

17. Common Avens or Herb Bennett, *Geum* **urbanum** L. ($\times \frac{2}{5}$); perennial herb growing in hedge-banks and on the borders of woods, and generally distributed, but rarer in the north of Scotland; the basal leaves (A, $\times \frac{2}{5}$) have longish stalks with a large end-lobe which is either shortly 3-lobed or divided to the base into 3 separate leaflets; stem-leaves variably lobed from above the middle to nearly the base; stipules (B, $\times \frac{2}{5}$) large and leafy; flowers terminal and solitary; sepals 5, united in the lower part, with a small bracteole between each; petals (C, $\times 2\frac{1}{2}$) bright yellow; stamens (D, $\times 8$) numerous; carpels numerous, free, in fruit (E, $\times \frac{4}{5}$) produced into a hooked prickle (F, $\times 2\frac{1}{2}$) (family *Rosaceae*).

This plant flowers from late spring till autumn, and the fruits are readily distributed by means of the hooked prickles, which catch on to the clothing of passers-by and the coats and fur of animals. Nectar is secreted by a green fleshy ring within the stamens. Cross-pollination is effected by insect visitors, and self-pollination is also possible. The plant was formerly used in medicine and the roots to impart a clove-like flavour to ale.

A second species of the genus is also found in Britain. This is the Water Avens, *Geum rivale* L., which grows in marshy places and ditches, and is common in northern England, Scotland, and Eire. In this the petals are orange streaked with red, and where the two species grow together hybrids between them are often found.

51

18. Common Agrimony, *Agrimonia eupatoria* L. ($\times \frac{2}{5}$); perennial herb found in dry thickets, hedge-banks, and sides of fields, and in waste places, where it grows more luxuriantly up to 3 ft. high. No basal leaves, but only stem leaves, pinnate with coarsely toothed leaflets (A, $\times \frac{2}{5}$), with numerous smaller leaflets between, and large leafy stipules (B, $\times \frac{2}{5}$) at the base; whole plant covered with soft hairs; flowers (C, $\times \frac{1}{2}$) in a stiff terminal spike, with a 3-lobed bract (D, $\times \frac{2}{5}$) below each; calyx-tube top-shaped, with a ring of hooked bristles at the top, becoming furrowed and hard in fruit (E, $\times 1\frac{1}{4}$), lobes 5, without intermediate bracts; petals (F, $\times 1\frac{1}{5}$) yellow; stamens 15–20, or fewer; carpels usually 2, in fruit enclosed by the hardened calyx (family *Rosaceae*).

This species was formerly a favourite remedy for liver complaints and a multitude of other diseases, and the whole plant yields a yellow dye. It flowers in summer and autumn, and the individual flowers remain open for three days. The flowers are adapted to both cross- and self-pollination. When they first open, the anthers are well away from the stigma, leaving ample room for an insect visitor to dust pollen on it from another flower or plant. Later they bend towards the stigma, rendering possible self-pollination, and finally the anthers drop off.

The floral axis (receptacle) is dry and woody and furnished with numerous stiff hooked bristles and acts as a fruit, the one or two real fruits (achenes) being enclosed by it. This false fruit readily attaches itself to clothing and to animals, by means of which it is widely distributed.

19. Gorse, *Ulex europaeus* L. (× ⅖); shrub, or rarely a tree up to 20 ft. high; flowers golden-yellow, slightly scented, in spring and early summer, and again in autumn; each branchlet and leaf ends in a sharp spine; calyx with blackish hairs outside, divided into two large lobes (A, nat. size); standard-petal bilobed at the apex (B, × 1½); wing-petals hairy on the lower side (C, × 1½); keel-petals also hairy (D, × 1½); stamens 10, all united into a sheath (E, × 2), the anthers alternately large and small, the large attached at the

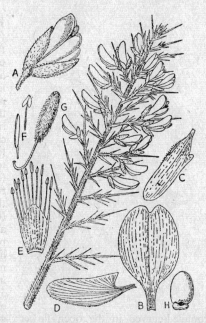

base, the small in the middle (F, × 4); ovary (G, × 1½) densely hairy; stigma terminal; pod ¾ in. long, densely hairy. On a warm day the pods burst with a little crack and fling out the seeds; these are brown and shining and have at the base a large fleshy aril (H, × 3) (family *Papilionaceae*).

Some consider the spiny character of the gorse to be the result of its environment, as it grows most frequently in exposed dry places in shallow and often stony soil. They point out that many plants which grow in deserts are also spiny. Others say that the spines have been developed to protect them from browsing animals. It seems probable that a combination of the two reasons supplies the answer; that spines in gorse and other plants are a direct outcome of environment (exposure, drought, and soil), and, once formed, have been retained because of the protection they afford. The flowers have no nectar, but bees alight on the wings and release the pollen with an explosive action which dusts their bodies below.

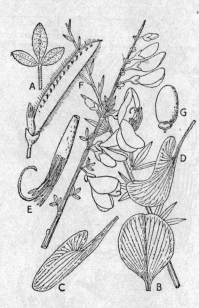

20. Broom, *Cytisus scoparius* (L.) Link ($\times \frac{2}{5}$); shrub up to 5 ft. high; branches numerous, long, straight, and whip-like, angular; leaves (A, $\times 1\frac{1}{4}$) divided into 3 small leaflets; flowers forming leafy racemes, bright yellow; calyx gaping and 2-lipped, lips minutely-toothed; standard-petal (B, $\times 1\frac{1}{4}$) broad and rounded, notched at the apex; wing-petals (C, $\times 1\frac{1}{4}$) oblong, with a rounded lobe; keel-petals (D, $\times 1\frac{1}{4}$) bent like a golf-club; stamens (E, $\times 2$) all united into a tube, 5 long and 5 shorter; ovary hairy on the margins; style rounded-curved in the open flower; stigma terminal; pods (F, nat. size) compressed, about $1\frac{3}{4}$ in. long, margins covered with long slender hairs; seeds (G, $\times 3$) several, broadly oblong, with a large fleshy aril at the base (family *Papilionaceae*).

Though there is no nectar, humble and honey bees visit the flowers and set in motion a very interesting explosive mechanism which releases the stamens and style from within the petals. The anthers are concealed within the boat-shaped keel-petals, and discharge their pollen very early, and it collects in the front part of the keel. When the insect alights on the keel and wings, the weight of its body presses them down and the pollen is discharged on to its undersurface, whence it is carried away and deposited on the stigma of another flower.

Broom tops, both fresh and dried, are used in medicine as a slight stimulant for the kidneys. The green angular switch-like branches are quite flexible and are useful for basket-work. When peeled they have the appearance of cane.

RESTHARROW, *Ononis repens* L.

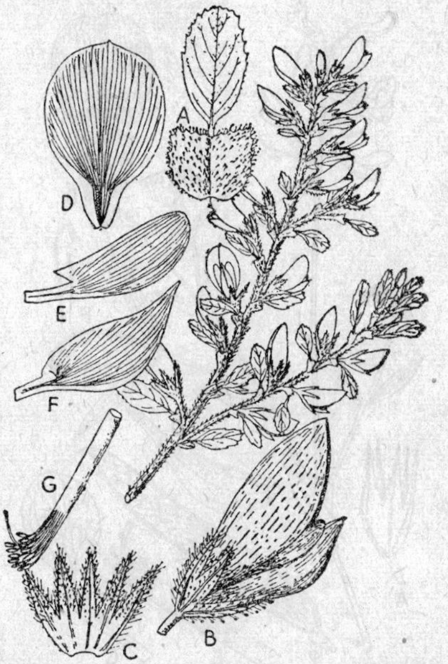

21. Restharrow, *Ononis repens* L. (× $\frac{2}{5}$); diffuse spreading herb; branches densely leafy, covered with long weak whitish several-celled hairs; leaflet (A, × $1\frac{1}{2}$) 1, with a large leafy stipule adnate to the very short stalk, oblong-obovate, rounded at the top and sharply toothed, covered with very short sticky glandular hairs; flowers (B, × $1\frac{1}{4}$) axillary, solitary, shortly stalked, pink, the standard streaked a deeper shade; calyx (C, × $\frac{4}{5}$) equally and rather deeply 5-lobed, lobes lanceolate, with long slender hairs and numerous short gland-tipped hairs; standard (D, × $1\frac{1}{5}$) rounded-obovate, with many nerves, slightly apiculate; wing-petals (E, × $1\frac{1}{5}$) oblong, blunt, with an acute basal lobe; keel-petals (F, × $1\frac{1}{5}$) beaked; stamens (G, × $1\frac{3}{5}$) all united into a closed sheath; style slender, with an apical stigma; pod about as long as the calyx, with 2 or 3 seeds (family *Papilionaceae*).

Restharrow flowers in summer and autumn and grows in grassy places, dry pastures and sand-dunes; it is partial to calcareous soil. The flowers have no nectar, but bees visit them to collect the pollen, which is squeezed out of the pollen-chamber formed by the tip of the keel-petals when these are depressed by the weight of the insect.

The genus *Ononis* may be recognised particularly by the stamens, which are all united together into a single sheath (monadelphous), and not in two bundles (diadelphous) as in most other members of the family to which the Broad Bean and Garden Pea belong.

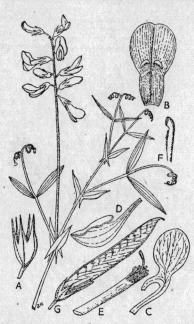

22. Meadow Pea, *Lathyrus pratensis* L. ($\times \frac{2}{5}$); perennial herb with creeping rootstock; stems weak, sharply angular; stipules arrow-shaped (sagittate); one pair of lanceolate very acute leaflets with 3 parallel nerves, and a terminal simple or branched tendril; flowers bright yellow, about $\frac{3}{4}$ in. long, several on an axillary common stalk (peduncle); calyx (A, $\times 1\frac{1}{4}$), equally 5-lobed; standard (B, $\times 1\frac{1}{2}$) contracted in the middle, notched at the apex, bearing an oblique appendix on each side; wing-petals (C, $\times 1\frac{3}{5}$) with a recurved hook-like lobe; keel-petals with a folded upper margin (D, $\times 1\frac{3}{5}$); stamens (E, $\times 2$) all united into a sheath; style (F, $\times 6$) with a terminal oblique stigma and a line of hairs on the upper side; pods (G, $\times \frac{4}{5}$) $1\frac{3}{4}$ in. long, compressed, smooth; seeds globose, smooth, dark brown or olive mottled with black, with a scar; widely distributed into Asia (family *Papilionaceae*).

The only other yellow-flowered species in Britain is the much less common *Lathyrus aphaca* L., mainly found as a cornfield weed in the south. It has no real leaflets, but large leafy stipules. The observer may find some difficulty in distinguishing the genus *Lathyrus* from *Vicia*, the Vetches (see figs. 23, 24). In *Lathyrus* the stigma is as described above, namely, with a line of hairs on the upper side below the stigma, whilst in *Vicia* there is a bunch of hairs as shown in figure 23, F.

Although the stigma of the flower of this species is surrounded by the pollen of the same flower, automatic self-pollination apparently does not take place, the stigmatic surface needing to be rubbed by visiting bees before it becomes receptive.

23. Common Vetch, *Vicia sativa* L. ($\times \frac{2}{5}$); long cultivated as a fodder plant and widely distributed in temperate regions; annual or biennial herb, with weak ribbed ascending stems; leaflets 4–7 pairs, obcordate to narrowly linear (the narrow-leaved form is regarded as the wild or ancestral form of *V. sativa* and is usually distinguished as *V. angustifolia* Roth), with a longish point in the middle of the usually V-shaped apex; common stalk ending in a single or branched tendril; stipules (A, $\times 1\frac{1}{4}$) leafy, much lobed, and with a dark spot in the

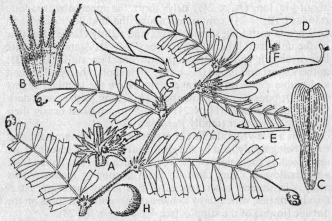

middle; flowers reddish-purple, axillary, solitary, or in pairs, on very short stalks; calyx (B, $\times 1\frac{1}{4}$) 5-lobed to the middle; standard (C, $\times 1\frac{1}{2}$) contracted below the middle, V-shaped at the top; wing-petals (D, $\times 2$) with a long backwards-directed lobe; keel-petals (E, $\times 1\frac{1}{2}$) with a shorter lobe; ovary hairy; style bent; stigma terminal, with a beard-like tuft of hairs (F, $\times 3$); pod (G, $\times \frac{1}{2}$) about 2 in. long, smooth, twisted after opening; seeds (H, $\times 1\frac{1}{2}$) several, rounded, dark brown, velvety, with a short narrow scar.

Other British kinds of Vetch have very shortly stalked flowers; these are *V. lutea* L., with solitary yellow flowers and hairy pod; *V. sepium* L., with 2–4 reddish-purple flowers on a short common stalk and smooth pods; *V. lathyroides* L., with much smaller flowers, small stipules, and granular seeds. The Bithynian Vetch, *V. bithynica* L., has longer flower-stalks and usually only 2 pairs of leaflets (family *Papilionaceae*).

24. Tufted Vetch, *Vicia cracca* L. ($\times \frac{1}{2}$).—This is the most easily recognised species because of the numerous bluish-purple flowers borne on one side of the flattened axis of the raceme; a perennial with slender annual stems up to 4 or 5 ft. high or even more, the whole plant hairy to nearly glabrous; leaves with numerous leaflets and the common stalk (rhachis) ending in a branched tendril; leaflets alternate to subopposite, linear to oblong, rounded at the apex and markedly pointed (mucronate); stipules divided into 2 lobes, but not conspicuous; flowers (see above) arranged in a dense raceme and more or less reflexed, about $\frac{1}{2}$ in. long (A, $\times 2\frac{1}{2}$); calyx short, the upper lobe broadest; standard (B, $\times 2\frac{1}{2}$) contracted above the middle; wings and keel-petals with long slender claws, and tightly clasped together by the unilateral lobes of the former (C, $\times 3$); stamens connate into a sheath split at the top with one free stalk (D, $\times 3$); anthers short and broad (E, $\times 10$); style shortly hairy all around and with a dense tuft of longer hairs below the terminal stigma (F, $\times 4$); pods (G, $\times \frac{3}{4}$) flat, about $1\frac{1}{2}$ in. long, with several dark velvety-brown seeds (H, $\times 2\frac{1}{2}$) $\frac{1}{6}$ in. diam., marked nearly their full length by a scar (family *Papilionaceae*).

When a bee visits the flower it settles on the wing-petals, and these, being firmly held by the keel-petals, act like a lever and are depressed by the weight of the insect, which deposits pollen from another flower. They close up again as soon as the latter flies away. In several other species of this genus there are extrafloral nectaries, which show as more deeply coloured spots on the outside (lower) of the stipules (see *Vicia sativa*, fig. 23).

This ornamental species is not likely to be confused with any others, except perhaps *Vicia orobus* DC. and *Vicia sylvatica* L., both of which have the flowers on a longish common stalk (peduncle) but have much fewer and paler flowers and broader leaflets; the leaf-stalk of *V. orobus* ends in a single point and not a branched tendril, and the stipules of *V. sylvatica* are much more toothed than in *V. cracca*.

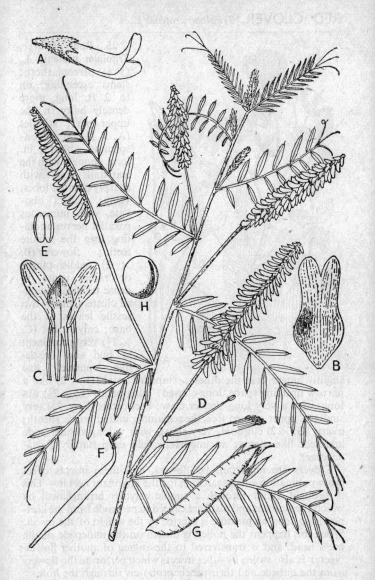

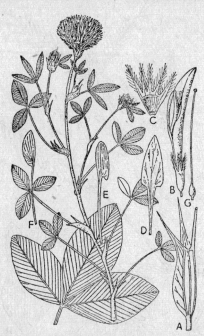

25. Red Clover, *Trifolium pratense* L. ($\times \frac{1}{2}$); perennial herb; stems ascending, up to 2 ft. long, more densely hairy in the upper part; stipules (A, $\times 1\frac{1}{2}$) very conspicuous, about $\frac{3}{4}$ in. long, connate with the leaf-stalk and with sharply pointed lobes, veiny; leaflets obovate, with numerous parallel nerves radiating into the minute teeth; flowers (B, $\times 2$) reddish-purple or rarely white, in dense terminal rounded clusters girt by two sessile leaves at the base; calyx-lobes (C, $\times 1\frac{1}{2}$) very prominent in bud and bristle-like, purple, one slightly longer than the others; standard petal (D, $\times 2$) like a narrow draining spade, long-clawed; wing-petals (E, $\times 2\frac{1}{2}$) oblong, with a very long slender claw; keel-petals (F, $\times 2\frac{1}{2}$) very similar; upper stamen free, the remainder united into a sheath; ovary (G, $\times 2$) ellipsoid, very short, with a long slender style and head-like stigma; an important field crop (family *Papilionaceae*).

Clovers are important bee-flowers, and these insects effect cross-pollination when searching for the abundant nectar. This is brought about through a simple valvular arrangement by which the stamens and pistil are caused to protrude from the keel-petals so long as pressure is exerted by the weight of the insect. When this happens the pollen is dusted on the underside of the bee's head, and is transferred to the stigma of another flower. Nectar is also stolen by other insects which perforate the flowers from the outside and thrust their proboscis through the hole.

26. White or Dutch Clover, *Trifolium repens* L. ($\times \frac{1}{2}$); perennial herb, with numerous spreading stems often rooting at the nodes; stipules inconspicuous, not $\frac{1}{2}$ in. long, with a short sheath and long narrow lobes; leaflets broadly obovate to rounded, sharply toothed, with a lighter band across the middle; leaf-stalks long; flowers (A, $\times 2\frac{1}{2}$) white or tinged with pink, in globose heads on a long (sometimes very long) common axillary stalk; individual flowers on slender stalks; calyx equally 5-lobed, not hairy; standard (B, $\times 2$) petal with a narrow claw with ridged margins, slightly notched at the apex; wing-petals (C, $\times 2$)

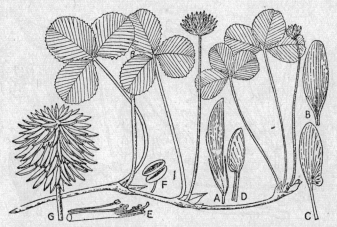

with an obtuse lateral lobe; keel-petals (D, $\times 2$) slightly joined, with slender claws; upper stamen free, the others united in a sheath split at the top (E, $\times 2\frac{1}{2}$); anthers (F, $\times 15$) very short, attached in the middle; style hairy only at the tip; pod with 2–4 seeds, enclosed in the withered corolla (family *Papilionaceae*).

The notes on pollination given for *T. pratense*, fig. 25, apply equally well to this species, which is also a valuable pasture and bee-plant. The genus *Trifolium* is quite richly represented in this country, there being over twenty native species. Some of these are very rare and of exceptional interest because of their geographical distribution; for example, two or three which are found only in Cornwall and in Spain and Portugal.

27. Bird's-foot Trefoil, *Lotus corniculatus* L. (× ½); perennial herb with long taproot; stems decumbent or ascending up to 1 ft.; leaves divided into 3 separate leaflets with a pair of large leaflet-like stipules at the base; leaflets obovate to ovate, slightly hairy; flowers about ½ in. long, in a cluster on a long common stalk, with 3 leaflets close under, bright yellow, the upper (standard) petal usually red on the outside; calyx (A, × 2½) with 5 sharply pointed equal-sized lobes, thinly hairy; standard (B, × 2) petal erect or recurved in the upper half, narrowed to the base with incurved margins; wing-petals (C, × 2) blunt; keel-petals

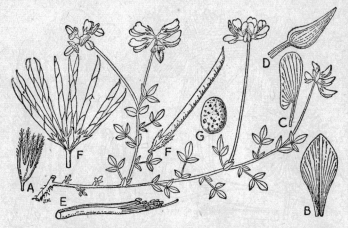

(D, × 2) beaked; one of the 10 stamens (E, × 2½) free from the others; pods (F, nat. size) linear, ¾–1 in. long, spirally twisted after opening; seeds (G, × 5) broadly ellipsoid, grey, mottled with dark brown (family *Papilionaceae*).

The back petal (standard or vexillum) is erect and often marked with red streaks which serve as nectar guides to bees, which effect cross-pollination. There is not space here to describe fully the wonderful floral mechanism of the pumping arrangement as it is called, by which the pollen, previously discharged into the tip of the keel-petals and held there by the elongated club-shaped stalks of the five outer stamens, is released. This is brought about by the weight of the insect pressing on the wing and keel petals. Self-pollination is ineffective because the stigmatic portion of the style must be rubbed before it becomes receptive to the pollen.

28. Great Sallow Willow, *Salix caprea* L. ($\times \frac{2}{5}$); tall shrub or bushy tree; winter buds (A, $\times \frac{2}{5}$) ovoid, with brown leathery smooth scales; leaves (B, $\times \frac{2}{5}$) broadly elliptic or obovate-elliptic, shortly pointed at the apex, base rounded to acute, rather wrinkled and irregularly crenate on the margin, cottony-hairy below; stipules leafy, usually soon falling; catkins very silky, the males (C, $\times \frac{2}{5}$) a little longer and thicker than the females (D, $\times \frac{2}{5}$), about 1 in. long; basal bracts densely silky; male floral bracts (E, $\times 1\frac{3}{4}$) with a fringe of long hairs at the top; stamens 2; anthers long-exserted from the bracts; female catkins about 2 in. long in fruit; bracts much narrower than in the male, with a small scale between the ovary stalk and the axis; ovary and style hairy (F, $\times 2$); fruits (G, $\times 2\frac{1}{2}$) about 1 in. long, silky, stalked; seeds (H, $\times 3$) narrow, with a fringe of long hairs from the base (family *Salicaceae*).

This Willow is rather variable and widely distributed, and there are several named varieties. It is common in all parts of our country, growing in woods and copses and in waste places. It is the only willow which commonly grows from seed, and in some places is almost a forest weed. It makes good fences, and sheep-hurdles made of it are said to last longer than those made of hazel. As it is so readily propagated by cuttings, it is useful for planting to hold the soil on river banks.

29. Bog-Myrtle, *Myrica gale* L. (flowering and leafy shoots ×
⅓); small shrub up to 3 ft. in boggy acid soils; stems purplish;
leaves produced after flowering, oblanceolate, toothed (serrate),
gland-dotted below (A, × ¾) and aromatic when bruised; male
and female flowers on separate plants (dioecious) produced before
the leaves in early spring; male spikes (B, × ⅓) catkin-like but
stiff, up to 1½ in. long; bracts broad, acuminate, below the
stamens (C, × 4) (no sepals and petals); filaments very short;
anthers 2-locular; female spikes (D, × ⅓) short and ellipsoid,

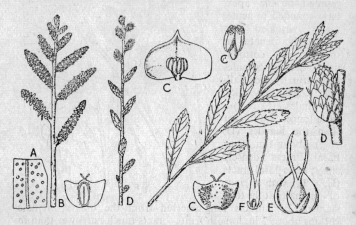

each flower (E, × 4) with an ovate bract, two scale-like sepals,
and a sessile ovary with two styles and one erect ovule; fruit
(G, × 3) small, winged (F, vertical section of female flower; ×
2½) (family *Myricaceae*).

The pollen is discharged from the anthers and falls on the
scales of the spike and is blown away in clouds by the wind. A
remarkable feature about the Bog Myrtle is that plants which
bear flowers of one sex during one season may change to the other
sex the next year.

It is only locally a common plant, and is found in lowland peat
bogs and on wet peaty slopes in various parts of the country.
Near London it is very abundant on Bagshot Heath.

30. Silver Birch, *Betula pendula* Roth. (A, leafy fruiting shoot, × $\frac{2}{5}$); a graceful tree with silvery-white papery bark; smaller branches pendulous; young branchlets glabrous except for scattered minute glands; leaves broadly triangular in outline, broadly wedge-shaped at the base, acutely acuminate at the apex, distinctly lobulate and the lobules toothed, with scattered glands on the upper surface when young; male catkins up to about 2 in. long, pendulous; female catkins about 1½ in. long and $\frac{1}{3}$ in. thick, very shortly and sparingly pubescent; scales (B, × 3) 3-lobed, the lateral lobes longer than broad and larger than the

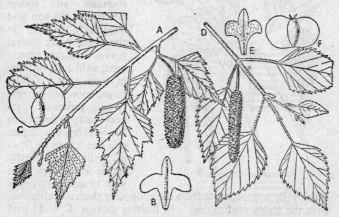

middle one, glabrous except for short hairs on the margins; fruits ("seeds") (C, × 3) with broad ascending membranous wings.

Red Birch, *Betula pubescens* Ehrh. (D, × $\frac{2}{5}$); similar to the above but young and two-year-old shoots densely covered with short soft hairs, more ovate and not lobulate leaves more or less simply toothed and more or less hairy below, especially in the axils of the nerves; rather narrower female catkins, the scales (E, × 3) more equally 3-lobed with the lateral lobes about as long as broad, and the fruit (F, × 3) with more horizontally spreading wings with a tuft of hairs at the top of the fruit-body.

These two Birches were formerly regarded as one rather variable species and called *Betula alba* Linn. Hybrids between them are common. Birches provide valuable timber and birch brooms; wood used principally for furniture, utensils, clogs, etc. (family *Betulaceae*).

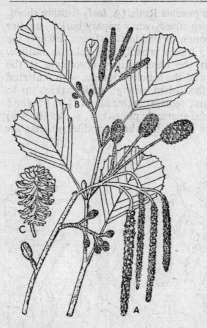

31. Alder, *Alnus gluti-nosa* Gaertn. ($\times \frac{2}{5}$); moderate-sized tree with dark foliage, flowering in early spring before the leaves, the catkins formed in the previous autumn; leaves obovate, rounded to wedge-shaped at the base, rounded or widely notched at the top and irregularly toothed in the upper part; lateral nerves straight, prominent, with tufts of hairs in their axils; stipules large, soon falling off; flowers unisexual (monoecious); male catkins (A, $\times \frac{2}{5}$) few in a cluster and pendulous in flower, with broad nearly sessile scales, each male with 12 stamens; female catkins (B, $\times \frac{2}{5}$) separate from the male, very short and ellipsoid, with the styles protruding; old fruiting catkins (C, $\times \frac{2}{5}$) with loose open scales like a small fir cone; nuts small and seed-like, not winged; the pollen is carried by the wind (family *Betulaceae*).

The timber of the Alder is used for making artificial limbs, brush-backs, general turnery, toys, etc. The tree is very widely spread through nearly all Europe, Siberia, Western Asia, and in Algeria and Morocco. It grows in wet woods, borders of streams and low-lying wet fields. The behaviour of the seeds is interesting. These are shaken out of the " cones " by the wind during autumn and winter, and their shells have air-tight cavities which enable them to float in water, and they secrete an oil which protects them from wet. If they fall in water, they float undamaged during winter, germinating in spring, the young seedlings at length drifting to the banks where they establish themselves.

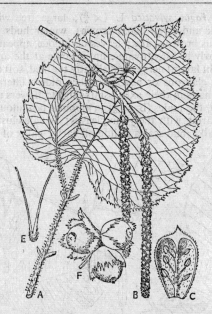

32. Hazel-Nut, *Corylus avellana* **L.**; shrub or small much-branched tree; young shoots (A, × ½) clothed with gland-tipped hairs; leaves more or less orbicular, widely cordate, shortly acuminate, coarsely and doubly toothed with several prominent lateral nerves; stipules lanceolate; flowers unisexual (monoecious), males very numerous in pendulous catkins (B, × ½), females (D, × ½) in a sessile scaly cluster, and with protruding red stigmas; scales of male catkins (C, × 3½) each with two adherent scales within bearing the stamens (about 8); female flowers (E, × 3½) 2 within each scale; ovary small with two long styles; fruits (F, × ⅔) solitary or clustered on a stalk, each hard nut partly enclosed by a leafy jagged involucre; the edible portion is the embryo, which enlarges to fill the nut when ripe; flowers in early spring before the leaves (family *Corylaceae*).

The shoots of the hazel are used for making walking-sticks, hurdles, crates, etc., and living specimens are bent or partially cut and interlaced for fencing. The slender one-year-old shoots that spring up from the roots are quite useful for basket-making.

33. Beech, *Fagus sylvatica* L. ($\times \frac{2}{5}$); large tree with thick smooth trunk and large dense crown; winter buds (A, $\times \frac{2}{5}$) with numerous brown scales; leaves deciduous, appearing with the flowers early in May, ovate-elliptic, acute at the apex, with several straight lateral nerves and slightly toothed, soft and silky when young, glabrous or nearly so when older; lateral nerves with tufts of hairs in their axils; stalks short; flowers unisexual (monoecious), the males (B, $\times \frac{2}{5}$) in globular pendulous stalked clusters appearing with the young leaves; female clusters on a short erect stalk; bud-scales falling off early; calyx of the male

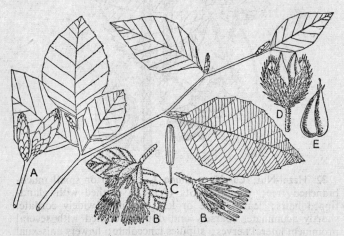

deeply 4–6-lobed, covered with long silky hairs; no petals; stamens (C, $\times 2$) about 8, on rather long slender filaments; anthers oblong, rather large; ovary of the female flower 3-locular, with 2 pendulous ovules in each division; styles 3; fruits enclosed in a hard bristly involucre (D, $\times \frac{2}{5}$) splitting low down into 4 divisions and containing 2–3 sharply 3-angular nuts (E, $\times \frac{1}{2}$) crowned by the small narrow sepals and style (family *Fagaceae*).

This is one of the largest and most important of our native trees. It occurs as far east as the Caucasus and north to southern Scandinavia. In Britain it is common in chalky districts such as the North and South Downs and the Chilterns, where there are local industries using the valuable timber for chair-manufacture, tool handles, etc., and it provides excellent firewood. The nuts are a favourite food for pigs.

34. Pedunculate Oak, *Quercus robur* L. and Sessile Oak, *Quercus petraea* (Matt.) Liebl. ($\times \frac{2}{5}$); there are two native species of oak in Britain, and they are so similar to each other that they were formerly often regarded as varieties or forms of one species; there are rather good differences, however, the pedunculate oak, *Quercus robur* L. (synonym *Quercus pedunculata* Ehrhart), having very shortly stalked leaves which are ear-shaped (auriculate) at the base, and are quite glabrous beneath, whilst the acorns are borne on a slender common stalk (peduncle); in the sessile

oak, *Quercus petraea* (Matt.) Liebl. (synonym *Quercus sessiliflora* Salisb.), the leaves have fairly long stalks, are wedge-shaped at the base, hairy beneath (especially between midrib and nerves), and the acorns are sessile on the branch or borne on a very short stalk (family *Fagaceae*).

Most people can recognise an oak tree, and the above description is probably sufficient. The pedunculate oak is more naturally adapted to a wettish soil, and is essentially a tree of the plains and low hills in northern latitudes, and is found wild in the greater part of Europe, Asia Minor and the Caucasus; the sessile oak is not found in the plains, favours less wet places, and ascends quite high up the mountains—for example, up to 5,300 ft. altitude in the Pyrenees.

The flowers are unisexual and produced in spring as the leaves unfold. The uses to which these fine trees can be put are legion, and they have played an important part in the history of our race, for shipbuilding and constructional work of all kinds, besides being good firewood.

35. Wych Elm, *Ulmus glabra* Huds.; a tree; mature leafy branchlets (A, × $\frac{1}{3}$) with purplish bark and marked with a few small brown lenticels, slightly hairy; mature leaves all with a small nearly glabrous bud in their axils, very unequal-sided at the base, elliptic or slightly obovate-elliptic, rather long-pointed (acuminate) at the apex, averaging about $5\frac{1}{2} \times 2\frac{1}{2}$ in., rather densely hairy in the axils of the main nerves below and in the fork towards the margin, otherwise very thinly hairy; lateral nerves about 15 pairs, most of them forked and forming a prominent Y $\frac{2}{3}$ towards the margin; margin doubly and rather coarsely toothed (serrate); leaf-stalk short and

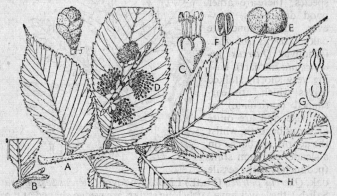

pubescent; stipules (B, × $\frac{1}{3}$) oblong-spathulate, about $\frac{1}{2}$ in. long, soon falling off; flowers (C, × $1\frac{1}{2}$) bisexual, appearing in early spring, arranged in clusters (D, × $\frac{1}{3}$) and at first enclosed by broad usually deeply notched brown hairy bracts (E, × $\frac{2}{3}$); calyx (C) top-shaped, 5-lobed to about the middle, pale and thin, the lobes obovate and flushed with crimson and fringed with short brown hairs on the margin; stamens 5; anthers (F, × 4) large, at first bright crimson, becoming purple after opening and releasing the minute white pollen; ovary (G, × $1\frac{1}{3}$) sessile, 2-locular, bright green, compressed, with pink stigmas; fruit (H, × $1\frac{1}{4}$) thin and compressed, about $\frac{3}{4}$ in. long; pollination by the wind, or failing that automatic self-pollination; all the flowers of one cluster not open at the same time; the filaments grow out rapidly from the bud before they shed their pollen, which only escapes in dry weather (family *Ulmaceae*).

36. Wall Pellitory, *Parietaria ramiflora* Moench. ($\times \frac{2}{5}$); perennial herb with long pubescent stems, often erect the first year and afterwards spreading or procumbent, usually on old walls, and in waste, stony places, flowering the whole summer; leaves alternate, entire, oblanceolate to elliptic, with slender stalks, apex rather bluntly acuminate, usually with only 2 pairs of lateral nerves, closely dotted on both sides with small cystoliths (A, $\times 1\frac{1}{2}$); no stipules; flowers in small dense sessile axillary clusters surrounded by a small involucre of a few bracts, bisexual (male and female) or

unisexual (one sex); male and bisexual flowers (B, $\times 4$) with a short 4-lobed calyx and 4 stamens opposite the lobes; female (C, $\times 4$) flowers with a tubular shortly 4-lobed calyx, which adheres to the seed-like or nut-like fruit (D, $\times 3$); seed (E, $\times 3$) solitary with a long embryo (family *Urticaceae*).

A peculiarity of this plant is that some stigmas are red and others white. They protrude from the bud of the bisexual flowers whilst the calyx is still shut up, and are shrivelled up before this opens and the anthers release their pollen. This is brought about by an explosive mechanism similar to that of the nettles. Their stalks are incurved in bud, and when this opens they expand and spring out, scattering their pollen in a small cloud. Gardeners are familiar with a related plant, the so-called Artillery plant (*Pilea muscosa* Lindl.), the flowers of which burst open with little explosions when syringed.

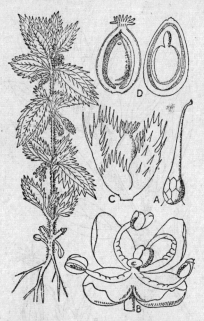

37. Small Stinging Nettle, *Urtica urens* L. ($\times \frac{2}{5}$); erect annual covered with stiff stinging hairs (A, × 15); leaves opposite, ovate or elliptic, coarsely toothed, 3-nerved from the base; flowers without petals, unisexual (**monoecious**), the males and females intermixed and arranged in loose axillary stalked or almost sessile clusters; male flowers (B, × 15) with 4 obovate sepals and opposite each a stamen which is incurved in bud and springs outwards and scatters the pollen when the flower opens; ovary rudimentary in the male flowers; female flowers (C, × 15) with 4 unequal-sized sepals, some with bristly hairs on the back; ovary ovoid, with a sessile papillous stigma; fruit (D, × 12) a small nutlet containing a single erect seed; grows mostly in waste and cultivated places, often as a garden weed, but more easily destroyed than the common stinging nettle (*Urtica dioica* L.), which is a perennial with flowers in branched spikes, and broader ovate stalked leaves (family *Urticaceae*).

The smaller stinging nettle has been described and figured here because everyone knows the ordinary kind. Some, however, who have not the necessary botanical knowledge, mistake the two Dead-Nettles for the common nettle because of the similarity in their leaves. One of these Dead-Nettles, *Lamium purpureum*, is shown in figure 191, and the flowers are very different from those of the stinging nettle. *Lamium album* L. has larger, white flowers. The leaves of the larger stinging nettle are valuable as a source of chlorophyll, used in medicine, etc., and the stems yield a very tough fibre.

38. Rock Rose, *Helianthemum nummularium* (L.) Mill. ($\times \frac{1}{2}$); low spreading shrublet partial to limestone and chalky soils, with a short much-branched woody stem; branchlets produced annually up to a foot long, hairy; leaves opposite, shortly stalked, oblong-lanceolate to almost ovate, entire, green and glabrous or nearly so above, hoary or white beneath and hairy with branched hairs (A, $\times$ 20); stipules (B, $\times \frac{3}{4}$) lanceolate, up to $\frac{1}{4}$ in. long; flowers in a terminal

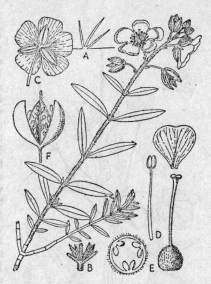

raceme, usually only one or two out at a time, the stalks deflected after flowering; sepals 5, three larger (C, $\times \frac{1}{2}$) with prominent ribs and two quite small; petals bright yellow or rarely white, spreading, soon falling off; stamens (D, $\times$ 5) numerous; ovary (E, $\times$ 5) short, hairy, 1-locular with the ovules attached to the walls; style bent, rather long, with a head-like stigma; capsule (F, $\times 1\frac{1}{2}$) splitting into 3 valves with the seeds attached to the middle of each; (E1, cross section of ovary, $\times$ 3) (family *Cistaceae*).

There is no nectar in the flowers of this species, but insects visit them to collect the pollen, of which a large quantity is produced by the numerous stamens. These radiate away from the mature stigma, and cross-pollination is effected by insects alighting in the middle of the flower and carrying pollen from other blossoms. If these fail, automatic self-pollination takes place through the flowers closing at night or during wet weather.

When not in flower this species is easily detected because of the opposite stipulate entire leaves clothed with branched hairs. Such hairs are not very common amongst British plants, though they are very general in the *Malva* family (*Malvaceae*), and in some of the Crucifers (*Cruciferae*).

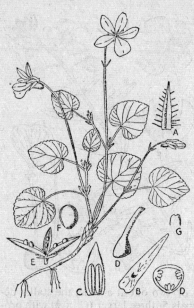

39. Wood Violet, *Viola riviniana* Reichb. ($\times \frac{2}{5}$); perennial, the slender rootstock covered with the persistent bases of the previous season's leaves; leaves broadly ovate, widely cordate at the base, crenulate, closely gland-dotted on both surfaces, long-stalked; stipules (A, $\times 1\frac{1}{2}$) conspicuous, narrowly lanceolate, with long comb-like teeth on the margin; flowers solitary in the upper leaf-axils, blue; stalks long, with a pair of narrow bracts about 1 in. below the flower; sepals (B, $\times 2\frac{1}{2}$) lanceolate, peltately attached at the base; petals obovate, veiny, the lowest produced into a large blunt grooved spur about $\frac{1}{3}$ in. long; anthers (C, $\times 2\frac{1}{2}$) sessile, the connective produced at the apex; ovary (D, $\times 2\frac{1}{2}$) with 3 placentas on the walls, and a stout oblique style; capsule (E, $\times 1\frac{1}{4}$) splitting into 3 boat-shaped parts which spread horizontally and bear the rounded smooth seeds (F, $\times 3\frac{1}{2}$) in the middle (G, grooved spur, $\times \frac{1}{2}$).

The genus *Viola* belongs to the family *Violaceae,* which is mainly found in tropical regions. There it is chiefly represented by trees and shrubs, so that those who have only seen our British species can have a very poor idea of the family as a whole. That is the reason the family is included amongst the woody plants, *Viola* being a very highly evolved member of the family and largely herbaceous, though there are several woody exotic species.

74

40. Heartsease, *Viola tricolor* L. (aggregate) ($\times \frac{3}{4}$); a very variable species divided by some botanists into several; usually grows in cultivated ground or rarely in pastures or river shingles; distinguished from other native violets by the mixture in the flower colour, though this is not constant, and by the leafy much-divided stipules; leaves spoon-shaped or ovate-elliptic, on long stalks, crenate, very shortly pubescent; flowers axillary, the stalks longer than the leaves, usually a mixture of purple white and yellow, usually the upper petals tinged or tipped with purple;

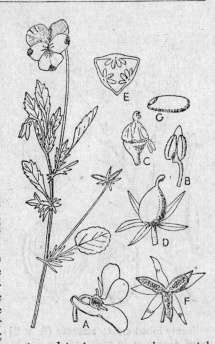

sepals oblong-lanceolate, about $\frac{1}{3}$ in. long, green; lower petal (A, $\times \frac{1}{2}$) spurred at the base; anthers (B, $\times$ 3) with produced connective; ovary (D, $\times$ 4) 1-locular, with ovules on the walls (E, $\times$ 6); capsule (F, $\times \frac{1}{2}$) $\frac{1}{3}$ in. long, smooth; seeds (G, $\times$ 2) like little brown eggs (family *Violaceae*).

This species of *Viola* have usually large, brightly coloured flowers, the lower petal of which is produced at the base into a spur in which the nectar is secreted. The anther of each of the two lower stamens is provided with a nectar-secreting process which projects into the spur of the lower petal. An insect probing for the nectar touches the stigma and deposits on it pollen from another flower. In addition to the ordinary flowers, some species possess flowers which do not open and have only rudimentary petals, but which produce fertile seed. These are called cleistogamous flowers.

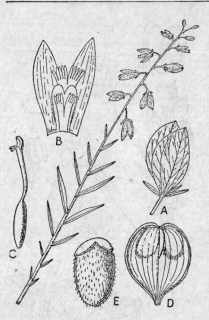

41. Milkwort, *Polygala vulgaris* L. ($\times \frac{2}{5}$); small perennial with tufted base, and numerous spreading or ascending branches up to 1 ft. long; leaves alternate, narrowly lanceolate to linear, entire, glabrous or nearly so; lower leaves shorter and broader; flowers in slender terminal racemes, with a small bract at the base of each stalk; sepals (A, $\times$ 2) 5, the two inner ("wings") much larger than the outer, obovate and veiny and resembling petals; petals (B, $\times 2\frac{1}{2}$) united with the stamens, bright blue or pink, the lowermost tipped with a deeply lobed crest; stamens (B, $\times 2\frac{1}{2}$) united into 2 bundles with 4 anthers in each and opening by a terminal pore; style (C, $\times$ 3) gaping at the top; fruit (D, $\times 3\frac{1}{2}$) compressed, broadly obovate, margined with a narrow wing, notched at the top; seeds (E, $\times 6\frac{1}{2}$) hairy, with a large caruncle (family *Polygalaceae*).

The flowers vary much in colour, and the chief means of attracting insects are the two large lateral petal-like sepals, the petals mainly serving to protect the stamens and pistil. Pollination mechanism is very interesting. The style has a spoon-shaped process near the stigma, which is a sticky hook-shaped protuberance. The anthers are so placed that when they shed their pollen it falls into this spoon, where it is stored while the stamens wither. An insect probing for nectar secreted at the base of the flower first encounters the pollen in the spoon and then the stigma, but it is not until the proboscis of the insect has been smeared with sticky matter from the stigma that the pollen adheres to it and is then carried to another flower.

42. **White Bryony,** *Bryonia dioica* Jacq. ($\times \frac{1}{3}$); rootstock thick and tuberous, often branched; stems climbing over hedges and bushes, rather fleshy; tendrils arising by the side of the base of the leaf-stalk, usually unbranched, spirally twisted; leaves dotted on both sides with short sharp bulbous-based hairs, deeply divided into 5 or 7 lobes, these again angular-lobulate, widely cordate at the base, main nerves radiating from the top of the leaf-stalk, the latter shorter than the leaf; flowers unisexual, the males (A, $\times 1\frac{1}{4}$) on one plant, the females on another

(dioecious); males few in axillary stalked racemes, the females (D, $\times \frac{2}{5}$) 2–4 on a very short common stalk, smaller and less conspicuous than the male; male calyx-lobes 5, very small and narrow; corolla (B, $\times \frac{4}{5}$) yellowish green, 5-lobed, up to $\frac{3}{4}$ in. diam., with oblong nervose lobes; stamens 5, two pairs joined together, the fifth separate, anthers wavy; ovary (C, $\times \frac{4}{5}$) below the calyx; style 3-lobed; berries (E, $\times \frac{2}{5}$) red or orange, about $\frac{1}{3}$ in. diam., with several flattish seeds (family *Cucurbitaceae*).

This plant is not found in Scotland and Eire. The fleshy tuberous rootstocks have caused poisoning to those who have eaten them in mistake for turnips or parsnips. The berries are poisonous.

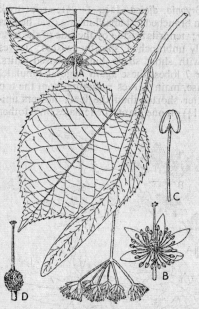

43. Lime-tree, *Tilia europaea* L. (× ½); large handsome tree up to 120 ft. high; leaves alternate, stalked, rounded - ovate, pointed at the apex, heart-shaped at the base, sharply serrate, hairy below particularly in the axils of the nerves (A, × ¾); flowers (B, × ⅘) few in an umbel, pendulous on a long stalk provided with a large narrow veiny bract and adnate to it in the lower half, sweet-scented and rich in nectar; sepals 5, not overlapping in bud; petals 5, greenish-white; stamens (C, × 3) numerous, shortly united at the base into clusters; ovary (D, × 1¼) globose, hairy, with a long slender style and radiate stigmas; fruit a small globose nut with 1 or 2 seeds; pollination by honey bees which cling to the stamens and stigmas (family *Tiliaceae*).

This tree is now known to be a hybrid between *T. cordata* Mill. and *T. platyphyllos* Scop., and it is probably the only hybrid upon which a genus has been founded. The wood has been extensively used for carving, turnery, toys, etc. *Tilia* is still included in the Pharmaceutical Codex, though it is now rarely used in medicine. The drug consists of the dried flowers of this and other species with their attached bracts, which are collected when fully expanded. These are stored in well-closed containers and protected from the light, and should not be used after more than twelve months from the date of collection. As a domestic remedy it is given in the form of a fresh infusion.

44. Dwarf Mallow, *Malva neglecta* Wallr. ($\times \frac{2}{5}$); procumbent annual of roadsides and waste places; stems hairy; leaves on long stalks, orbicular, deeply cordate at the base, slightly 5 – 7 - lobed, toothed (crenate); stipules conspicuous, lanceolate; flowers clustered in the leaf-axils, on slender hairy stalks, small, pale blue, about 1 in. diam.; sepals 5, lanceolate, with an epicalyx of small bracts; petals broadly notched, veiny; stamens (A, $\times$ 1½) united into a tube, the anthers at first forming a cone over the stigmas and curving away from the latter on opening; stigmas emerging after the opening of the anthers and cross-pollinated by insects; if this fails they curl amongst the anthers and may be self-pollinated; carpels (B, $\times$ 1⅖), 10–15, hairy, forming a disk-like fruit with the persistent sepals like a rosette; seeds (C, $\times$ 5) kidney-shaped; flowers spring to autumn (family *Malvaceae*) (synonym *Malva rotundifolia* L.).

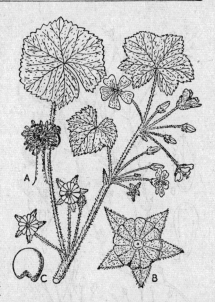

The chief characters of the *Malva* family are that the calyx-lobes do not overlap each other in bud (valvate), and that the stamens are united into a single column around the styles (monadelphous). Another interesting feature is the 1-locular anthers, due to the splitting of the connective. Altogether it may be regarded as being a very highly evolved group, and some are of great commercial importance, such as Cotton, from the genus *Gossypium*. The stems of many *Malvaceae* are very fibrous, probably an indication that they have been evolved from arboreal ancestors, such as the Lime-tree family, *Tiliaceae*.

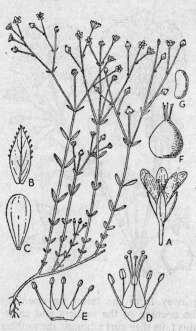

45. Purging Flax, *Linum catharticum* L. ($\times \frac{2}{5}$); a small delicate erect or subdecumbent annual in meadows, pastures, and heaths especially on calcareous soils and sandy dunes; stems very slender, glabrous; leaves opposite, without stipules, the lowermost short and elliptic, the upper oblanceolate, pale glaucousgreen, 1-nerved; flowers (A, $\times 2\frac{1}{2}$) very small, arranged in lax terminal cymes, each on a slender stalk; middle flowers maturing first, and already in fruit before upper ones bloom; sepals (B, $\times 3$) 5, with a few short gland-tipped hairs on the upper half of the margin; petals (C, $\times 3$) 5, white; stamens (E, $\times 5$) 5, united in the lower part into a cupular tube around the base of the ovary; styles 5, free, with head-like stigmas; capsule (F, $\times 5$) with the 5 cells divided by a membranous partition, each with a single seed (G, $\times 4$); related to the flax-plant, *Linum usitatissimum* L., but differing from this and other native species by the opposite leaves and tiny white flowers (family *Linaceae*).

The staminal tube secretes on its outer side five drops of nectar from five small flat pits situated in the middle of the filaments. The five petals are inserted a little above the nectar pits, giving access to the nectar. The anthers are at the same level as the stigmas but at first remote from them, so that cross-pollination may take place. Failing this self-pollination is brought about by the flowers closing in the evening and pressing the anthers against the stigma.

46. Dog's Mercury, *Mercurialis perennis* L. (female plant, × ⅔); rootstock slender, creeping, the roots covered with fine hairs; stems unbranched, erect, up to about 15 inches high, covered with short stiff spreading hairs; leaves stalked, opposite, each with a pair of stipules at the base of the stalk, elliptic to oblong-lanceolate, more or less acute at the apex, rounded at the base, toothed (crenate) on the margin, thinly hairy on both surfaces; flowers unisexual, the male and female on separate plants (dioecious), arranged on slender axillary common stalks as long as or longer than the leaves; male flowers (A, × 5) small and green, in clusters on the stalk; calyx 2-3–lobed; no petals; stamens 9-12, radiating from the middle of the flower; anthers rounded; female flowers (B, × 5) single or paired on the common stalk; calyx as in the male; no petals; ovary 2-lobed, covered with stiff bristly hairs, with 2 spreading stigmas; fruit (C, × 5) a 2-lobed capsule, bristly hairy, each lobe with a single pendulous warted seed (D, × 8) (family *Euphorbiaceae*).

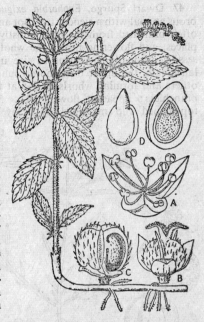

This grows in woods and shady places, flowering in early spring before the leaves of other plants are fully developed; a second native species is *M. annua* L., an annual, with branched stems, and the female flowers sessile or shortly stalked in the axils of the leaves. As in the nettle, the pollen from the male flowers is carried to the female by the wind. The anthers are at first yellow, but afterwards the cells diverge and scatter their pollen and become a beautiful indigo blue colour. Dog's Mercury is poisonous to stock.

81

47. Dwarf Spurge, *Euphorbia exigua* L. ($\times$ $\frac{1}{3}$); small glabrous annual with a slender tap root and erect or ascending stem often branched from the base, mostly in cultivated and waste places, and flowering nearly the whole year; leaves alternate, sessile, gradually increasing in size upwards, linear to linear-lanceolate, the upper ones more rounded at the base than the others and forming whorls of 3–5 at the base of the flowering branchlets; apparent flowers (A, $\times$ 5) consisting of a short top-shaped cup margined by fleshy elliptic glands (B, $\times$ 8)

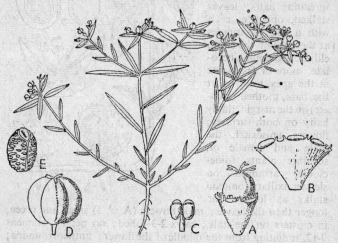

between which are two short awl-shaped lobes; stamens very few, short, each representing a male flower; anthers rounded, opening across the top (C, $\times$ 5); ovary shortly stalked within the cup and representing the female flower; styles 3, spreading, 2-lobed; fruit (D, $\times$ 4) 3-lobed, opening into the 3-loculi, each of which contains a single transversely warted seed (E, $\times$ 4) (family *Euphorbiaceae*).

There are several species of this genus in our islands, interesting because the apparent flower is really an aggregation of several males and one female, girt by an involucre of bracts margined by glands. Good characters for distinguishing the species are to be found in the shape of these glands and in the seeds, some of which are warted or wrinkled, or deeply pitted.

48. Petty Spurge, *Euphorbia peplus* L. (× ⅔); annual, erect or ascending, usually branched from the base, up to about 1 ft. high, glabrous in all its parts; stem leafy, the leaves increasing in size upwards, alternate, obovate, with slender stalks, the upper ones becoming sessile; flowers (A, × 2½) very small, surrounded and almost hidden by the broad upper leaves; each apparent flower consists of a cup-like involucre (B, × 3) of united bracts bearing conspicuous crescent-shaped glands (C, × 3½) on the margin,

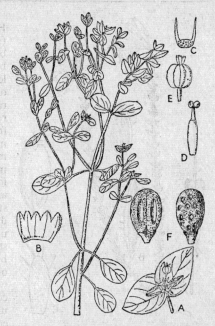

each gland with a long tail at each end; male flowers (D, × 7) consisting of a single stamen jointed in the middle, with 2 rounded anther-lobes opening across the middle; female flower (E, × 7) composed of a single ovary supported on a stalk in the middle of the male flowers; ovary deeply 3-lobed, with 3 short bifid styles, 3-locular, with 1 ovule in each compartment; fruit a 3-lobed capsule, splitting into 3 lobes, each lobe containing a single grey seed (F, × 4½) deeply pitted on the back and with two large elongated cavities on the inner face (family *Euphorbiaceae*).

The glands of the involucre secrete a shallow layer of exposed nectar; pollination mainly by flies, beetles and wasps; a common weed in cultivated and waste places, seeding very rapidly; it flowers during the whole summer and autumn; a tincture and a liquid extract of the whole plant have been recommended for asthma and bronchial catarrh (see also notes accompanying fig. 47).

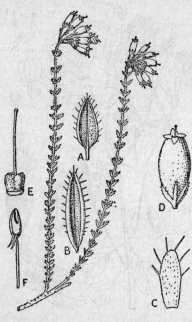

49. Cross-leaved Heath, *Erica tetralix* L. ($\times \frac{2}{5}$); low shrublet branched from the base; branches pubescent; leaves (A, $\times 4$) in whorls of 4, rather densely arranged, shortly stalked, rather variable in width from narrow with the margins recurved to the midrib to broader and markedly papillous below (B, $\times 5$), furnished also with rather long stiff hairs; flowers drooping in a terminal umbel-like cluster; stalks bearing a leafy bract; sepals (C, $\times 4$) oblong, finely hairy and with a few bristly hairs; corolla (D, $\times 1\frac{3}{4}$) tubular but narrowed to each end, shortly 4-lobed; stamens 8, the anthers (F, $\times 2\frac{1}{4}$) with 2 long appendages at the base; ovary (E, $\times 2$) truncate at the top, pubescent; style a little longer than the corolla; fruit with a very thin shell; often grows with the common heather but much less abundant; flowers in late summer (family *Ericaceae*).

Pollination is by bees. The flowers are nodding or pendulous and the nectar is secreted in a blackish annular ring around the base of the ovary. As the blackish sticky stigma occupies the mouth of the corolla or beyond it, an insect visitor hanging on to the corolla and probing for the nectar must first touch this, some of the sticky substance adhering to the proboscis. When it probes into the flower the anthers are shaken by the insect touching the horn-like processes at their base and the pollen falls on its head, adhering to the part made sticky. It is thus carried to another flower, when the process is repeated. As the proboscis of the honey bee is rather short it commits burglary by using the hole made by other bees.

50. Bell Heather, *Erica cinerea* L. ($\times \frac{2}{5}$); a low woody undershrub, much branched from the base; stems very shortly hairy; leaves (A, $\times 1\frac{3}{5}$) usually 3 in a whorl, often with short shoots in their axils, very shortly stalked, short and needle-like, acute, the margins recurved and meeting together on the lower surface; flowers (B, $\times 1\frac{3}{5}$) in interrupted clusters in the upper part of the shoot and borne on short shoots; sepals linear-lanceolate, acute, keeled, with narrow membranous margins; corolla reddish purple, ovoid in outline, about $\frac{1}{4}$ inch long, gaping at the mouth and with 4 very small lobes; stamens (C, $\times 5$)

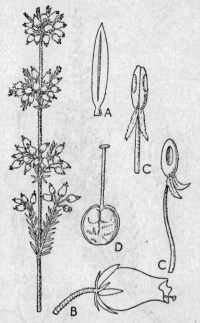

8, inserted below the ovary and free from the corolla; anthers included in the corolla-tube, opening by pores, with two toothed appendages at the base; ovary (D, $\times 5$) globose, style shortly exserted from the corolla, with a terminal head-like (capitate) stigma; capsule enclosed in the corolla-tube, with numerous minute seeds (family *Ericaceae*).

This species flowers in summer and autumn, and covers large tracts of moorland country often in company with *E. tetralix* L. (fig. 49) and the common heather, *Calluna vulgaris* (L.) Hull (fig. 51).

The nectar is secreted around the base of the ovary and the flowers are pollinated by insects as described under *Erica tetralix* (fig. 49), the bells being often perforated by bumble bees.

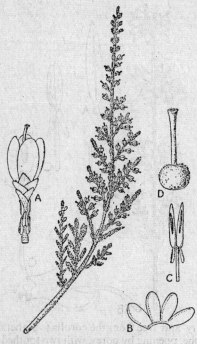

51. Scotch Heather or Ling, *Calluna vulgaris* (L.) Hull ($\times \frac{2}{5}$); a small shrublet sometimes up to 2 ft. or so high, but usually dwarfer, much branched; branches softly hairy with very short hairs; leaves opposite, arranged in 4 rows on the young shoots, very small, produced at the base below the point of insertion, softly hairy or at length glabrous; flowers (A, $\times$ 3) arranged in leafy racemes, small, each subtended by a few triangular bracts fringed with hairs; sepals 4, coloured pink like the corolla or very rarely white, dry and scarious; corolla (B, $\times$ 3) deeply 4-lobed, much shorter than the calyx; stamens 8; anthers (C, $\times$ 4) with 2 tails at the base, opening by a long pore-like slit; ovary (D, $\times$ 4) depressed-globose, hairy; style stout, protruding beyond the calyx; fruit a small capsule opening by slits between the loculi; often dominant on moors with acid soils, and very common in Scotland; flowers from July to early September (family *Ericaceae*).

The Scotch heather is a very valuable bee-plant, heather honey being greatly preferred by some people. Beehives are a familiar sight on heather moors, to which they are transported before the heather flowers open in late summer. Nectar is secreted by eight little swellings between the stamens at the base of the flower.

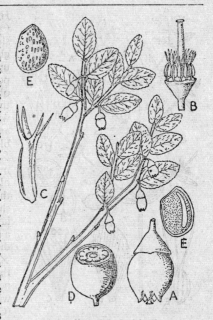

52. Bilberry, Blueberry, Whortleberry, *Vaccinium myrtillus* L. ($\times \frac{2}{5}$); small much branched erect glabrous shrublet up to about 1 ft. high; branchlets somewhat flattened but distinctly angular or almost winged; leaves deciduous, alternate, ovate-elliptic, very shortly stalked, minutely toothed (crenulate); flowers (A, $\times 1\frac{1}{4}$) solitary in the leaf-axils, shortly stalked, pendulous; calyx combined with the inferior ovary, not lobed; corolla greenish and tinged with red, with a globose tube and short lobes; stamens (B, $\times 1\frac{1}{4}$) twice as many as corolla-lobes, free from the corolla; anthers (C, $\times 3$) with two longish horns at the back; ovary inferior; style stout, undivided; fruit (D, $\times 1\frac{1}{4}$) formed of the ovary and calyx united together, a globose berry, blue-black and covered with a glaucous bloom like that of a black grape; seeds (E, $\times 4$) with a long slender embryo (family *Vacciniaceae*).

Grows on mountain and hilly heaths and woods often with heather; berries an important food for grouse and used locally for tarts and jam. The flowers are without odour, but are rich in nectar. This is secreted around the base of the style. The corolla hangs more or less downwards and only bees with a proboscis long enough to reach to its base are able to act as pollinating agents. When a bee inserts its proboscis into the corolla it strikes against the horns on the back of the anthers, causing the pollen to fall out on to the visitor's head. When visiting another flower this is likely to be brushed against the stigma, which projects beyond the mouth of the corolla.

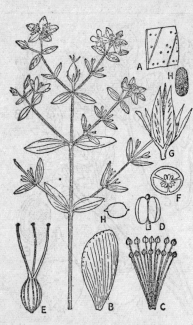

53. St. John's-Wort, *Hypericum perforatum* L. (× ⅖); perennial with short runners and erect glabrous 2-ridged stems up to 1½ ft.; leaves opposite, sessile, ovate-oblong, 3-nerved from the base, entire, marked with transparent dots and sometimes a few black spots below (A, × 3); flowers in a terminal leafy cyme, the oldest flower terminating the main and lateral shoots; sepals 5, lanceolate, entire, marked with a few gland-dots or glandular lines; petals (B, × 2) twice as long as the sepals, free, many-nerved and margined with glands; stamens (C, × 2½) numerous, shortly united into 3 bundles; anthers (D, × 7) rounded, tipped by a globular gland; ovary superior (E, × 3), with 3 slender free styles, 3-locular, with numerous ovules attached to the central axis (F); fruit (G, × 2) divided into 3 segments, marked with glandular globules outside; seeds (H, × 3) finely reticulate; flowers in summer and autumn; (H, cross section of stem showing ridges) (family *Hypericaceae*).

St. John's-wort is easily recognised by the opposite, entire (not toothed) leaves, which if held up to the light show a number of small transparent dots, and by the stamens being united into bundles or phalanges as they are called. There are no stipules. There are many handsome garden plants among the numerous species of this widely spread genus. The 3 spreading styles are placed between the bundles of stamens and the anthers do not touch the stigmas, so that cross- and self-pollination depend on insect visitors.

54. Holly, *Ilex aquifolium* L. ($\times \frac{2}{5}$); an erect much-branched evergreen tree or large bush; stem smooth, dark green; leaves alternate, shortly stalked, ovate or elliptic in outline, but often rather deeply lobed, the lobes ending in a sharp prickle, often the upper leaves of a tree quite entire, leathery in texture and dark green; flowers (A, $\times 1\frac{1}{2}$) in small axillary clusters, shortly stalked, sometimes unisexual; calyx of small short lobes; petals white, obovate, united at the base into a very short tube (B, $\times$

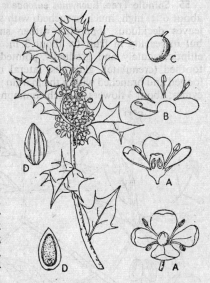

$1\frac{1}{2}$); stamens as many as the petals and inserted between them on the inside of the tube; no disk; ovary 4-locular, with one pendulous ovule in each division; stigmas 4, forming a disk-like plate on the top of the ovary; fruit (C, $\times \frac{4}{5}$) a red berry enclosing 4 little stones each containing a seed (C, $\times 2\frac{1}{2}$) (family *Aquifoliaceae*).

The common holly should be the least troublesome tree to identify, as it is so well known in connection with Christmas festivities. Few people, however, are familiar with the flowers, which are produced in summer. The wood of the holly is very hard and is the lightest in colour of our native timbers. It is therefore valuable in marquetry work. Bird-lime may also be made from holly bark. The well-known Maté or Paraguay tea is obtained from a South American species of this genus, *Ilex paraguensis* St. Hil.

55. Spindle Tree, *Euonymus europaeus* L. ($\times \frac{2}{5}$); a shrub up to about 6 ft. high, much branched, with short twiggy branchlets; leaves deciduous, opposite, rather small at flowering time, but increasing in fruit to about 3 in. long and 1½ in. broad, elliptic, acutely and gradually pointed, closely but obscurely toothed (crenulate), glabrous, lateral nerves about 7–8 pairs, looped and branched within the margin; flowers in little axillary cymes, about 3 flowers on each common stalk, the middle flower

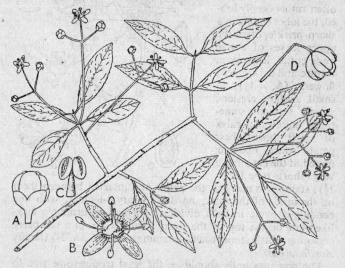

(B, $\times 1\frac{1}{4}$) opening first, yellowish green; sepals 4, green, rounded; petals 4, oblong, overlapping in bud (A, $\times 2$); stamens (C, $\times 3$) 4, inserted on a thick disk; anthers facing outwards; ovary hidden in the disk, with a short undivided style; fruits (D, $\times \frac{1}{2}$) usually 4-lobed, red to pink, opening into the lobes, the seeds covered by a yellow fleshy aril (family *Celastraceae*).

The Spindle Tree is poisonous in all its parts. The wood is hard and used for making butchers' skewers, and it makes excellent artists' charcoal. In addition to the flowers shown, unisexual ones also occur, with vestiges of the opposite sex. Cross pollination is effected by insects, the anthers, which face outwards, opening before the stigmas are receptive. Nectar is secreted in the fleshy disk surrounding the base of the style.

56. Buckthorn, *Rhamnus cathartica* L. (male flowering shoot, × ⅖); shrub with numerous spreading branches, the branchlets often ending in a short stiff thorn; leaves deciduous, elliptic or ovate-elliptic, increasing in size when the fruits develop (A, × ⅘), pubescent on the nerves below to glabrous or nearly so, shortly toothed (serrulate) on the margin; flowers green, unisexual, dioecious, borne in clusters at the base of the young shoots, the males (B, × 2½) on slender stalks (pedicels); sepals 4, united into a tube at the base, lanceolate, 3-nerved; petals (C, × 3½) 4, very small and narrow, inserted at the mouth of the calyx-tube, each with a stamen opposite; stamens longer than the petals; anthers

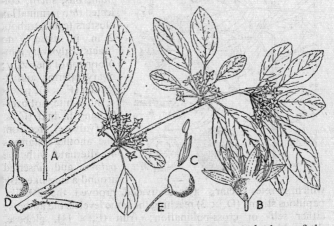

facing inwards (introrse); rudimentary ovary at the base of the calyx-tube; female flowers with rudiments of stamens and smaller petals; ovary (D, × 3), with a 3–4-lobed style, and 1 erect ovule in each loculus; fruit (E, × ⅘) black, about the size of a pea (family *Rhamnaceae*).

Owing to the two sexes being separate, cross-pollination by insects is essential; the fact that each sex possesses rudiments of the other shows that the ancestral stock of this species had bisexual flowers, as are found in the second native species *R. frangula* L. The wood makes excellent gunpowder and charcoal, and the berries, which are poisonous, produce sap green for water colours.

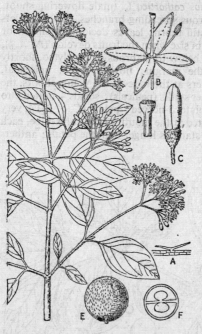

57. Dogwood, *Cornus sanguinea* L. ($\times \frac{2}{5}$): shrub up to about 6 ft. leaves opposite, without stipules, ovate, entire, thinly clothed below and on the flower-stalks, ovary and young fruit with white T-shaped hairs (A, $\times$ 4); flowers (B, $\times 1\frac{1}{2}$) numerous, small, collected into terminal lax clusters (cymes) about 2 in. in diam.; no bracts; calyx very minute on top of the ovary; ovary inferior and 2-locular (F, $\times$ 4); petals 4, dull white, not overlapping in bud (C, $\times$ $1\frac{1}{2}$) (valvate); free from one another; stamens 4, alternate with the petals, and inserted around a ring-like disk which secretes nectar; style undivided, grooved, the disk-like papillous stigma (D, $\times$ 3) reaching the same level as the anthers; either self- or cross-pollination; fruit (E, $\times 1\frac{1}{2}$), globose, fleshy, black, bitter, the hard inner stone (drupe) containing the seed (family *Cornaceae*).

A second native species, the Dwarf Cornel, *Cornus suecica* L., is widely distributed and has a slender creeping rootstock with annual stems only a few inches high. These have opposite ovate leaves, and a little terminal umbel of flowers surrounded by four large white petal-like bracts. The real petals are very minute and a dark purple colour. Certain continental botanists consider it distinct, its name being rather formidable, *Chamaepericlymenum suecicum* (L.) Asch. & Graebn.

Dogwood is common on limy soils in the south of England, but rare in the north. The slender annual shoots can be used for basket-making.

58. Ivy, *Hedera helix* ($\times \frac{2}{5}$); woody evergreen shrub or creeping on the ground or climbing up trees or walls to considerable height by means of sucker-like outgrowths; leaves alternate, thick, evergreen and shining, those lobed prominently nerved, those of the flowering shoots less lobed and ovate elliptic to obovate and sometimes broadly notched; petioles very variable in length; flowering branches short, from the main climbing stem, ending in an umbel of yellowish green flowers (A, × $\frac{2}{5}$; B, × 1$\frac{1}{4}$); calyx short, saucer-like, toothed; petals

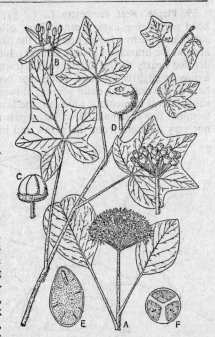

(C, × 1$\frac{1}{4}$) 4, free, not overlapping in bud; stamens 4, alternate with petals; ovary half-below the calyx but completely so in fruit, 3-locular; berry (D, × 1$\frac{1}{2}$) depressed-globose; seeds 2-5, with very small embryo and the seed-coat intruding into the abundant endosperm; flowers in late autumn, fruits lasting until spring and eaten by pigeons (E, vertical section of seed, × 1$\frac{3}{4}$; F, cross-section of fruit, × 1$\frac{1}{2}$) (family *Araliaceae*).

In this country the ivy is one of the latest plants to flower. Insects effect cross-pollination by crawling about amongst the flowers conveniently arranged in umbels, an abundance of nectar being secreted in a yellowish green disk. After the anthers have released their pollen they quickly drop off, and the stigma becomes receptive to pollen from other younger flowers, the disk secreting nectar more actively. If self-pollination takes place it is said to be ineffective, for in Sweden it failed to set seed when grown in a greenhouse, probably owing to the absence of insects.

59. Maple, *Acer campestre* L. ($\times \frac{2}{5}$); tree with a round
head with dense dark green foliage, often in hedges and th
sometimes bushy; leaves opposite, the base of the stalks meeti
around the branchlets; stalk slender; blade cordate at the bas
divided nearly to the middle into 5 (rarely 3 or 7) lobes, lob
entire or slightly lobulate, pubescent beneath especially at t
base of the radiating main nerves; flowers in cymes terminatir
short lateral branchlets, greenish, the lateral male (A, $\times$ 2), t
terminal flower female (B, $\times$ 2); sepals usually 5, narrow, a
not very different from the petals and inserted around a flesl

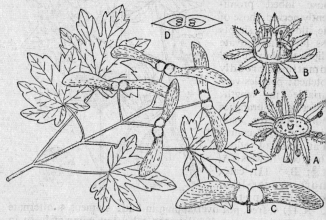

ring-like disk; stamens about 8, inserted within the disk which
covered with minute drops of nectar; ovary rudimentary in th
male flower, spreading within the disk in the female and 2-locular
styles 2, divergent; fruit (C, $\times \frac{3}{5}$) separated when ripe into
parts, spreading horizontally, each produced into a large vein
thin wing ("key"); seeds 1 or 2 in each part; found wild as fa
north as the Tyne, extending in Europe eastwards as far as th
Caucasus; the wood is beautifully marked and, when available
is employed for furniture and veneers, and turned into bowls
cups, etc.; a second species, *A. pseudo-platanus* L., the Sycamor
or Plane Tree, is introduced, and reaches a height of about 100 ft.
has more toothed leaf-segments, slender pendulous racemes, an
the "keys" of the fruit are less spreading; the timber is valuabl
(D, cross-section of ovary, $\times$ 4) (family *Aceraceae*).

60. Ash, *Fraxinus excelsior* L. ($\times \frac{2}{5}$); a tall handsome tree with elegant deciduous foliage; branches opposite; leaves opposite, pinnate, with 3-5 pairs of opposite leaflets, these lanceolate or ovate-lanceolate, acute or pointed, toothed (serrate), and with an odd terminal leaflet rather larger than the others; no stipules; flowers bisexual or unisexual, opening in spring before the leaves, arranged in opposite clusters (A, $\times \frac{2}{5}$) in the axils of the leaves fallen from the previous year's shoot; clusters surrounded by a few woolly scales; flower-stalks very short but elongating in fruit; no sepals and no petals; male flowers (C, $\times$ 3) with 2 stamens; anthers elliptic; ovary 2-locular, with a short thick style and 2-lobed stigma and often with 2 abortive stamens; fruit (D, $\times \frac{2}{5}$) a capsule produced at the top into a wing, in all about $1\frac{1}{2}$ in. long (E, vertical section of seed, $\times$ 2) (family *Oleaceae*).

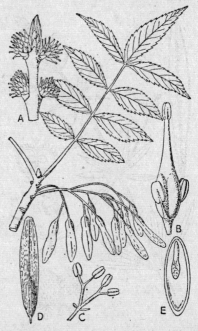

The flowers of the common Ash are pollinated by the wind and the large fleshy stigmas mature a few days before the anthers. The pollen is mealy and freely blows about. The wood of the Ash is a valuable, very tough timber, and used for many purposes. The branches, when split and steamed, are easily bent into various shapes and are employed in conjunction with willow, etc., for making the handles and framework of trug-baskets for the garden and farm. The Olive, *Olea europea* L., from which Olive oil is obtained, belongs to this family, as also the Lilac (*Syringa*).

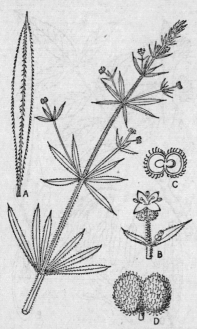

61. Cleavers or Goosegrass, *Galium aparine* L. (× $\frac{2}{5}$); a slender scrambling annual several feet long, clinging to bushes and hedges by means of short recurved hook-like hairs on the angles of the stems, the margins and midrib of the leaves; leaves (A, × $\frac{4}{5}$) and stipules 6–8 in a whorl, indistinguishable from one another, linear or linear-oblanceolate, tapered to the base, up to 2 inches or so long, ending in a long slender sharp point, midrib and margins covered with short, sharp hard recurved prickle-like hairs; flowers (B, × $1\frac{1}{2}$) very small, borne in small leafy clusters (cymes) in the axils of the upper leaves, soon developing into fruit; calyx completely reduced; corolla very short, with 4 spreading lobes which do not overlap in bud; stamens 4, inserted between the corolla-lobes, anthers small, on rather short filaments; ovary inferior, 2-locular and 2-lobed, covered with hooked hairs, each lobe (C, × $2\frac{1}{2}$) with a single ovule attached to the central axis; styles 2, free to the base, each with a single rounded stigma; fruits (D, × 2) divided into 2 rounded lobes, each densely covered with hooked bristly hairs; seeds solitary in each half.

The common name Cleavers alludes to the persistence with which the plant clings by means of the small hook-like hairs on the stems and leaves and bristly fruits. The family *Rubiaceae*, to which this plant belongs, is mainly found in tropical regions; it includes the quinine-producing *Cinchona*, and the Coffee plant.

FOXGLOVE

Digitalis purpurea

RAMSONS

Allium ursinum

BUCKBEAN *Menyanthes trifoliata*

MARSH MARIGOLD *Caltha palustris*

HENBANE

Hyoscyamus niger

LESSER CELANDINE   *Ficaria verna*

SLOE   *Prunus Spinosa*

TANSY

Tanacetum vulgare

CENTAURY

Centaurium umbellatum

COWSLIP
Primula veris

62. Lady's Bed-straw, *Galium verum* L. (× ⅘); rootstock woody, short and creeping; stems slender, ascending, often much branched from the base, up to about 15 inches high, covered with minute reflexed hairs; leaves in whorls of 6 to 8 (half of them stipules and half leaves, but these indistinguishable), linear or needle-like, acute, with recurved slightly rough margins, often with a short leafy shoot in their axils; flowers (A, × 5) numerous in an oblong panicle, each cluster in the axils of a whorl of small leaves, and each ultimate cluster has a whorl of small leafy bracts; flower-stalks smooth; calyx very minute on top of the inferior ovary; corolla 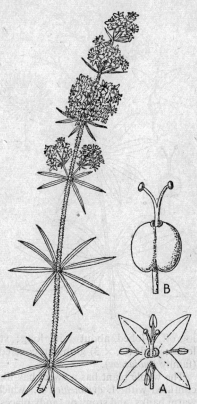 yellow, 4-lobed, the lobes spreading from the extremely short tube; stamens 4, inserted between the corolla-lobes; anthers oblong; at the mouth of the tube 2 fleshy disk-like bodies; ovary inferior, 2-lobed and 2-locular, with 1 ovule in each lobe; style with 2 branches and a head-like stigma to each; fruits (B, × 10) slightly 2-lobed, smooth (family *Rubiaceae*).

This species flowers more or less the whole summer in clumps on banks, dunes and pastures; the flowers smell strongly of cumarin and pollination is brought about mainly by the feet of insects crawling about among the flowers.

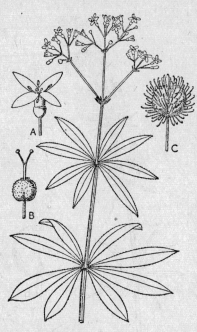

63. Woodruff, *Asperula odorata* L. ($\times \frac{4}{5}$); perennial with a slender creeping rootstock growing mainly among dead leaves under the shade of trees; stems erect, unbranched, angular, smooth; leaves in whorls of 8 (rarely fewer or more, composed of indistinguishable leaves and leafy stipules), oblanceolate, up to about 1½ in. long, mucronate at the apex, a few very short stiff hairs on the margin and below; below the whorls a ring of very minute bristles; flowers (A, $\times 3\frac{1}{2}$) in a terminal loose cyme, white; calyx very minute, above the inferior ovary (B, $\times 6$); corolla soon falling off, 4-lobed, about ¼ in. long; stamens 4, alternate with lobes; fruit (C, $\times 3$) globular, covered with fine hooked bristles (family *Rubiaceae*).

The whole plant has a sweet hay-like scent; not likely to be confused with *A. cynanchica* L., which grows in dry pastures, warm banks, and stony or sandy places, and which has only 2 or 4 much narrower leaves to each whorl, and smooth fruits. The Woodruff is intolerant of strong light and dies out immediately the tree-canopy is removed

The abundant nectar is concealed at the bottom of the corolla-tube and insects searching for it brush against the anthers above the entrance, transferring pollen from one flower to the stigmas of another. As in Cleavers (figure 61), the fruits readily adhere to the fur or skin of animals and are transported from place to place. Even considerable parts of the plants may be dragged by means of the rough margins of the leaves.

64. Elder, Sambucus nigra L. (× ⅖); a small spreading tree with rough bark, the stem and branches full of pith; young annual shoots from the main branches soft; leaves deciduous, opposite, pinnate, with an odd terminal leaflet, and 2 or 3 pairs of leaflets; leaflets opposite, shortly stalked, elliptic to obovate, acutely acuminate, rather sharply toothed, glabrous or nearly so; flowers (A, × 2) scented, numerous, arranged in flat terminal corymbs, with about 5 primary branches; no

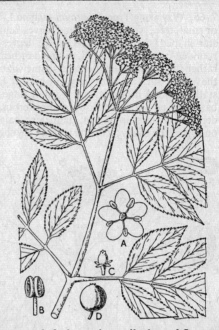

bracts; middle flower at each fork nearly sessile, lateral flowers stalked; sepals 5, very small and green; petals 5, yellowish-white, united at the base into a very short tube and spreading horizontally; stamens 5, alternate with the corolla-lobes, the rather large anthers (B, × 3½) facing outwards; ovary (C, × 3) at first nearly quite superior but becoming inferior in fruit; stigmas 3–5, sessile; fruits (D, × 1½) purple-black and juicy, densely arranged (family *Caprifoliaceae*).

This flowers in early summer and grows in woods and waste places; it is one of our most useful British plants, the fruit making excellent wine and jam or jelly; the flowers are used medicinally; the pith is employed by botanists for embedding specimens for section cutting; the wood is very hard and has been used by mathematical instrument makers and for butchers' skewers, shoemakers' pegs, etc.; leaves, avoided by stock, were formerly used to make an insecticide. Although the flowers of this species are scented, there is no nectar.

65. Wayfaring Tree, *Viburnum lantana* L. (× $\frac{2}{5}$); a large shrub or small tree; young shoots and leaves below covered with short star-shaped (stellate) hairs (A, × 3); leaves deciduous, opposite, rounded-ovate, not pointed, rounded or heart-shaped at the base, rather sharply toothed (dentate), somewhat wrinkled (rugose) on the upper surface, with very prominent lateral nerves below; stalks about ½ in. long, with a small ridge between them at the base, but no stipules; flowers odoriferous, small and white, in dense flat cymes up to 3 in. diameter; calyx-lobes 5, very small on top of the ovary; corolla with a very short tube and 5 spread-

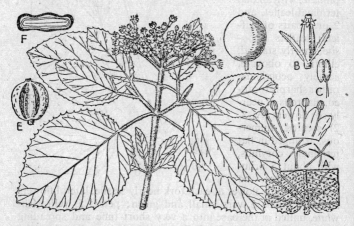

ing rounded lobes; stamens (C, × 4) 5, alternate with the lobes, and arising from the base of the tube; anthers rounded, facing inwards; ovary (B, × 4) below the calyx (inferior), with a small disk on top and 2–3 very short stigmas; fruit (D, × 1½) a purplish-black berry with one hard flattened seed (F, × 1½). (E, × 1¼, berry with flesh removed) (family *Caprifoliaceae*).

A hedgerow plant flowering in early summer, and mainly found in southern England. It is a widely distributed species, occurring all over temperate and southern Europe as far as the Caucasus. The stamens are curved inwards when the flower opens and the anthers are over the stigmas. Automatic self-pollination is therefore easy. Nectar is secreted in a flat layer on top of the ovary and immediately below the stigmas. Later the stamens spread towards the outside of the flower.

66. Guelder Rose, *Viburnum opulus* **L.** ($\times \frac{2}{5}$); a shrub or very small tree with attractive Hydrangea-like flowers arranged in a terminal umbel-like cluster (cyme); the outer flowers (A, $\times$ $1\frac{1}{2}$) are sterile and white, and serve to attract insects; garden forms often have all the flowers so transformed; the short leafy flowering shoots have brown bud-scales at the base; leaves opposite, rounded in outline but divided nearly to the middle into 3 or rarely 5 coarsely toothed and pointed lobes; principal nerves as many as the lobes and radiating from the base; leaf-stalks with a pair of sessile glands at the top (B, $\times \frac{3}{5}$), and towards the base

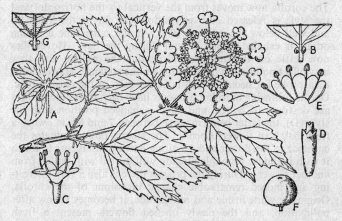

about 2 pairs of very narrow outgrowths, but no stipules; flowers (C, $\times 1\frac{1}{2}$) white, scented like hawthorn; sepals (D, $\times \frac{4}{5}$) 5, very small, above the ovary (ovary inferior); corolla (E, $\times 2$) short and 5-lobed; stamens 5, inserted at the base of the corolla-tube, the anthers facing inwards (introrse); ovary 1-locular and containing 1 ovule; fruit a small 1-seeded berry (F, $\times \frac{4}{5}$) (G, shows lower side of leaf) (family *Caprifoliaceae*).

Viburnum is a large genus and very widely distributed, with numerous species in eastern Asia, especially China, many of which are grown in our gardens. *V. opulus* flowers in early summer and ranges across Europe into Asiatic Russia and into the Arctic regions. Pollination is either by the agency of bees and other insects, or self-pollination may take place.

67. Honeysuckle, *Lonicera periclymenum* L. ($\times \frac{3}{4}$); probably our most lovely climbing shrub, with deliciously sweet-scented flowers. These exhibit most interesting features concerned with cross-pollination. The flower-buds (A) are at first vertical, and the anthers open within them between 6 and 7 p.m., the stigma becoming receptive at the same time; but it is placed higher than the anthers, so automatic self-pollination cannot normally take place (B, nat. size). The first flowers open about 7 p.m. The lower lip of the corolla separates first and the anthers stick out, the stigma still being held by the hook-like upper lip. The corolla now moves from the vertical to the horizontal and the style is released and curves down as far as the lower lip and well below the anthers (C). At the same time a strong odour is exhaled, which is faint during the day. Hover flies now settle on the anthers and devour the pollen, and they may effect pollination by alighting on the stigma. Hawk-moths then probe for nectar, which is at the base of the corolla-tube. On the following morning if insects have been there, the anthers are destitute of pollen, and have exchanged position with the style (D), the latter being in place between 7 and 8 p.m., when a fresh batch of flowers opens. The stigma now dominates the entrance to the flower and a visiting hawk-moth is sure to touch it with its body, probably already well dusted with pollen from another flower. During the process there is also a very interesting and indeed remarkable change in colour of the corolla. Originally white inside and red outside, it becomes yellow after pollination, and the newly opened flowers present a fresh attraction to hawk-moths, drawn from a distance by the fragrance of the flowers, when near, by the conspicuous collection of them (inflorescence), and when quite close, by the more clearly visible newly opened white flowers. Eventually the successfully fertilized flowers become a dirty orange brown and gradually lose their scent altogether. Humble bees sometimes visit honeysuckle, but find it difficult to reach the nectar, and they are not supposed to have had any influence in developing the special characters of the flower.

The leaves are opposite and not toothed (entire) and there are no stipules, though there is a connecting line between their bases. The calyx is glandular and on top of the ovary (ovary inferior), (E, $\times$ 5), and the corolla is 2-lipped, the upper lip of 4 united lobes, the lower of a single lobe. The red berries are crowded into a cluster (F, nat. size) (family *Caprifoliaceae*).

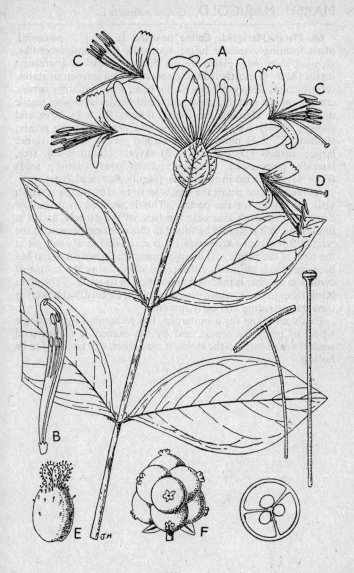

68. Marsh Marigold, *Caltha palustris* L. ($\times \frac{1}{2}$); perennial, often forming extensive tufts; rootstock thick and tuber-like, growing in marshy places by the side of brooks and streams; leaves (A, $\times \frac{1}{2}$) mostly from the rootstock, on long stout stalks, suborbicular, deeply cordate at the base, with radiating nerves, crenate on the margin, glabrous; stem leaves becoming sessile upwards and clasping the stem; flowers (B, $\times \frac{1}{2}$) large and showy; sepals 5–6, bright yellow and petal-like; no petals; stamens (C, $\times 5$) numerous, in several series; anthers rather large; carpels (D, $\times 2$; E, $\times 3$) several (about 6–10), free, laterally compressed, narrowed to the small stigma; seeds (F, $\times 4$) constricted in the middle (family *Ranunculaceae*).

As there are no petals the sepals serve to attract insects which visit the flower for the nectar. This is secreted in a shallow depression on each side near the base of the carpels, and it is interesting that it should be found in this position because in the related Buttercups (*Ranunculus*) it is concealed in a small pit at the base of the petals. It often happens that when an organ has been modified, reduced or dispensed with during the course of evolution another is modified to function in its stead. The plant is injurious to stock, which usually avoid it, especially at flowering time during spring and early summer.

Easily mistaken for a buttercup, but recognised by the single whorl of petal-like sepals, and by the numerous ovules (and seeds) in each carpel; the stems, if cut across, will be found to be hollow.

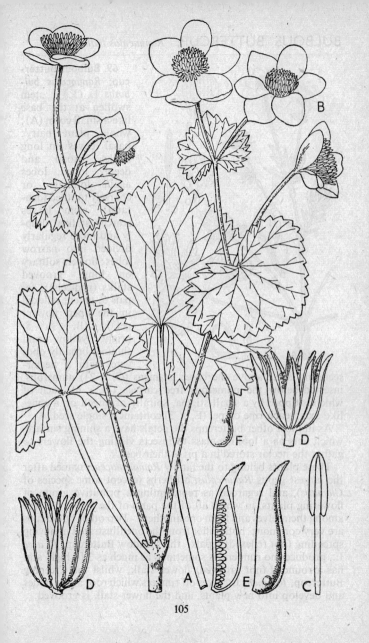

69. Bulbous Buttercup, *Ranunculus bulbosus* L. ($\times \frac{2}{5}$); stem swollen at the base like a small corm (A); whole plant hairy; basal leaves on long stalks, broad and deeply lobed, lobes again lobulate or coarsely toothed (dentate); stem leaves scarcely stalked, deeply and more regularly divided into narrow lobes; flowers solitary on long, grooved stalks (pedicels); sepals 5, green, reflexed in the open flower; petals (B, $\times \frac{4}{5}$) 5, bright yellow and shining, broadly obovate, with a nectar-secreting scale above the base; stamens (C, $\times 2\frac{1}{2}$) numerous, inserted below the numerous free carpels (D, $\times 6$), each of which is tipped by a small stigma, spirally arranged on a cone-like axis; each ripe carpel (E, $\times 3$) contains a single seed.

As in most other buttercups the petals have a shining surface, which acts as a looking-glass to insects visiting the flowers to gather the nectar stored in a pit at their base.

These plants belong to the family *Ranunculaceae*, named after the largest genus *Ranunculus*, all herbs (except some species of *Clematis*), and regarded as representing a primitive group of flowering plants, in which all of the parts of the flower are free among themselves and from one another. Two other buttercups are very common; both differ from the one illustrated in having spreading (not reflexed) sepals; the Meadow Buttercup, *R. acer* L., produces no runners, is sometimes as much as 3 ft. high, and has a rounded (not grooved) flower stalk, whilst the Creeping Buttercup, *R. repens* L., gives off runners which root at the nodes and develop into new plants, and the flower-stalk is grooved.

70. Spearwort, *Ranunculus flammula* L. ($\times \frac{2}{5}$); perennial of short duration or annual growing in marshes and wet fields and beside lakes and ponds; stems decumbent at the base and then erect, up to about $1\frac{1}{2}$ ft. high, with few ascending branches, glabrous and closely ribbed; radical leaves on long stalks with broad sheaths at the base, elliptic lanceolate, rather blunt, slightly dentate with very distant teeth on the margin, with 3–5 ascending subparallel nerves; stem-leaves becoming sessile on the broad membranous sheathing base, lanceolate to almost linear, becoming entire as they merge into bracts, nerves parallel to the midrib; flowers few, and forming lax corymbs, the older flowers in the middle of each fork; sepals remaining erect, rounded with a few minute hairs outside; petals (A, $\times 1\frac{1}{4}$) bright yellow, shining, obovate, with a nectariferous pit just above the base; stamens numerous (about 35); carpels (B, $\times 3$) numerous and free, with a very short stigma, in fruit forming a globose head, each carpel with a short hook-like point and a flat membraneous margin on one side (family *Ranunculaceae*).

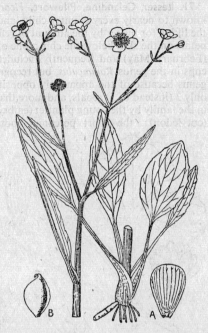

A few of our British buttercups have undivided leaves which at most are very slightly toothed, and with more or less parallel nerves as in some Monocotyledons, such as in the *Alisma* family, *Alismataceae* (see fig. 197). Indeed they are quite closely related to the family mentioned, which forms a link between the Dicotyledons and Monocotyledons.

71. Lesser Celandine, Pilewort, *Ficaria verna* Huds. (× ⅖); known to nearly every country child, and often used as a test of the liking for butter by the amount of reflection from the shining petals on the skin below the chin; one of the first spring flowers (February–May) and frequently included with the true butter-cups in the genus *Ranunculus*, but recognised here as a separate genus because of the apparently opposite unequal-sized leaves, only 3 (instead of 5) sepals, and more than 5 petals; remarkable in the family by the young plantlet (embryo) with only 1 seed-leaf (cotyledon); the short perennial rootstock bears numerous

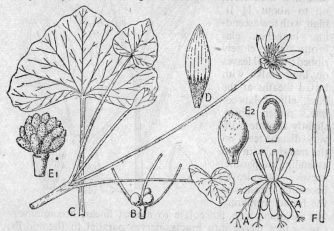

finger-like tubers, (A, × ⅖); frequently small rounded bulbils (B, × ⅖) in the axils of the leaves, especially plants growing in very shady places; lowest leaves (C, × ½) long-stalked, glossy, broadly triangular, all with wavy margins; flowers star-like, solitary, axillary, closing in bad or dull weather; petals (D, × 1¾) about 8 or more, an outer whorl of 3 alternate with the sepals, an inner whorl of 5, if more than these within the 5 ; broadly lanceolate, bright yellow and shining, with a dull deeper coloured nectar-secreting base, bleaching with age, stamens numerous; anthers (F, × 4) opening at the sides; carpels about 20–25 (E1, × 1½), free, with a subterminal sessile stigma not receptive until most of the anthers have shed their pollen, each carpel containing a single ovule attached at the side (E 2, × 2) (family *Ranunculaceae*) (synonym *Ranunculus ficaria* L.).

72. Wood Anemone, *Anemone nemorosa* L. ($\times \frac{2}{5}$); perennial with slender black rootstock, flowering in and near woods in early spring before the trees become leafy; leaves 2–3 from the rootstock, long-stalked, divided to the base into three parts, each part narrowed to the base and deeply lobed and coarsely toothed; flowering stem solitary, bearing a single terminal flower (A, $\times \frac{2}{5}$) and a whorl of 3 leaves towards the top like the root leaves but smaller and shortly stalked; sepals usually 6, glabrous, petal-like and white or mauvish pink to purple-blue; no petals; stamens

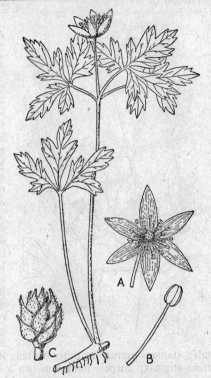

(B, $\times 2\frac{1}{2}$) numerous; filaments slender; anthers fixed at the base, short; carpels (C, $\times 1\frac{3}{4}$) free, short and beaked, hairy, narrowed into a beak; seed solitary in each carpel; easily distinguished from the much rarer *A. pulsatilla* L. (Pasqueflower), which has silky-hairy sepals and the carpels ending in feathery beaks like *Clematis* (family *Ranunculaceae*).

There are no nectaries in the Wood Anemone, but insects of many kinds visit it for the sake of its pollen. The absence of petals is perhaps best explained by assuming that they have been dispensed with during the course of evolution and their function, that of attracting insects, has been taken over by the sepals. These, in addition, protect the pollen by the flower bending over at night and during wet weather, so that they do double work.

TRAVELLER'S JOY, OLD MAN'S BEARD, *Clematis vitalba* L.

73. Traveller's Joy, Old Man's Beard, *Clematis vitalba* L. ($\times \frac{2}{5}$); large slender climber, spreading over trees, shrubs and hedges by means of the twisted leaf-stalks; branches softly pubescent, tough; leaves opposite, without stipules, pinnate, leaflets usually 5, ovate or ovate-lanceolate, 3-nerved from the base, entire or with a few coarse teeth, hairy on the nerves; flowers with a hawthorn-like odour, in loose axillary panicles, at the end of short axillary branchlets; sepals 4, not overlapping in bud (valvate), white or greenish white, softly hairy outside; no petals; stamens numerous, outer opening first and bending away from stigmas; carpels numerous, on a short axis, free, very conspicuous in fruit, forming a dense white mass with long silky hairs, the style elongated into a thread-like tail; seed solitary (family *Ranunculaceae*).

There is no nectar, but the pollen provides food for insect visitors. This species may cause injury to stock if eaten in quantity; the branches are useful for making light baskets. It is usually very common on calcareous soil, particularly on the North and South Downs in the south of England, flowers during summer, and is easily distinguished from other wild British plants by its climbing habit, opposite pinnate leaves, loose axillary panicles of flowers with a coloured calyx but no petals, and the bunch of hairy long-tailed fruits. It is widely distributed in Central and Southern Europe as far east as the Caucasus.

110

74. Field Poppy, *Papaver rhoeas* L. ($\times \frac{1}{2}$); annual, erect, up to about 2 ft. high, clothed with stiff spreading bristly hairs; lower leaves deeply pinnately divided, the divisions again deeply cut or coarsely toothed (serrate); flowers solitary on long stalks, nodding in bud and covered by two bristly hairy sepals which fall off as the flower opens (A, $\times \frac{1}{2}$); petals 4, overlapping and crumpled in bud, rich scarlet with a black eye at the base; stamens numerous, with slender filaments; ovary really 1-locular, but the placentas (B, $\times 1\frac{1}{2}$) extending from the walls nearly to the middle, broadly top-shaped with a disk-like top from the middle of which radiate the 8–12 sessile stigmas; capsule (C, $\times \frac{3}{4}$) more or less globose, crowned by the disk-like stigmas and opening beneath them by as many pores; seeds (D, $\times 8$) numerous, kidney-shaped, reticulate. (E, vertical section of seed, $\times 8$) (family *Papaveraceae*).

The common Poppy flowers all summer and is often very abundant in cornfields, frequently colouring the landscape. It is poisonous to stock in a green condition. There are no nectaries. Although the stamens are already mature in the bud stage and pollen from them falls on the already receptive stigmas, this self-pollination is ineffective, and later on cross-pollination is brought about by insects visiting the flowers for the pollen itself, as there are no nectaries in the flowers of the whole family.

Another feature of the family is the very fugitive nature of the sepals in many species, which usually fall off as the petals expand. The petals are usually crumpled in bud.

111

75. Horned or Sea Poppy, *Glaucium flavum* Crantz ($\times \frac{2}{5}$); a strong-growing annual on sandy or pebbly sea-shores, very glaucous; basal leaves (A, $\times \frac{2}{5}$) thick, stalked, up to 1 ft. long, deeply pinnately lobed, the lobes increasing in size upwards, these again coarsely toothed, loosely covered below when young with short hairs; stem-leaves sessile, ovate, less deeply lobed; flowers shortly stalked, the lower ones forming well-developed fruits whilst the upper are still open; sepals 2, falling off early, with a few crisped hairs outside; petals 4, yellow, about $1\frac{1}{2}$ in. long; stamens numerous; ovary linear, with 2 sessile stigmas; fruit elongated and slender, curved, up to 1 ft. long; the large petals fall off the second day after opening, and the stigmas develop before the anthers open and project beyond them, thus preventing self-pollination; there are no nectaries (synonym *Glaucium luteum* Scop.) (family *Papaveraceae*).

Although this plant belongs to the same family as the field Poppy (figure 74), to which its flowers bear some general resemblance, though they are yellow, its fruits are quite different, and are more like those of some of the Crucifer family (*Cruciferae*). Indeed the elongated fruits are the most conspicuous feature of the plant and mature very early. There are several connecting links between the Poppy and the Crucifer families, the latter being a more recent or highly evolved group.

76. Greater Celandine, *Chelidonium majus* L. ($\times \frac{2}{5}$); perennial; rootstock thick, fleshy, full of yellow juice which turns reddish when broken; leaves glaucous below, irregularly pinnate, the segments elliptic or obovate, coarsely toothed and often lobulate at the base on one side and resembling stipules; flowers in a loose umbel on a long common stalk (peduncle) opposite the leaf (leaf-opposed); calyx minute; petals 4, yellow, soon falling; stamens (A, $\times 1\frac{3}{5}$) several; ovary linear, with a very short style and small head-like stigma; fruit (B, $\times \frac{4}{5}$) cylindrical, smooth, up to

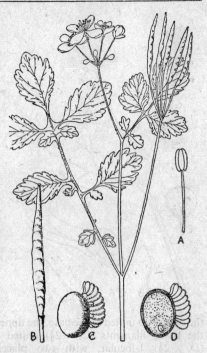

about 2 in. long; seeds (C, $\times 2\frac{1}{4}$) with a large crest on one side; flowers all summer and grows on roadsides and in waste places often near houses and occasionally in neglected gardens; flowers remain closed during dull weather, and the anthers then open in bud and effect self-pollination; open flowers are pollinated by bees collecting pollen; no nectaries; juice of root reputed to cure warts; injurious to stock.

This species is rather different from other members of the Poppy family (*Papaveraceae*) to which it belongs, but is not likely to be confused with any other in the British flora because of the position of the flower cluster (inflorescence), whose stalk is placed opposite to a leaf. Only one or two other common herbs share this striking feature, namely the Fumitory (*Fumariaceae*) (figure 77) and *Senebiera didyma* (*Cruciferae*) (figure 90). The fruits are similar to those of some *Cruciferae*.

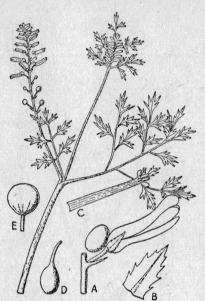

77. Fumitory, *Fumaria officinalis* L. ($\times \frac{2}{5}$); annual, glabrous all over, pale green, often forming a dense spreading tuft up to a foot or two in diameter; leaves bipinnate, the ultimate segments often coarsely 3-toothed or lobed; flowers (A, $\times$ 2) in slender racemes opposite the leaves (leaf-opposed) or terminal, the lower often developed into fruits before the upper have finished; stalks short, in the axil of a small bract; sepals (B, $\times$ 4) 2, white or coloured, toothed; petals 4, dull purple, with dark coloured tips, in two pairs, the outer two united at the base, the upper with a large pouch at the base; filaments (C, $\times 2\frac{1}{2}$) united into a sheath; ovary (D, $\times 2\frac{1}{2}$) 1-locular, with two placentas and two ovules on the walls; fruit (E, $\times$ 2) a 1-seeded nut, nearly globose (family *Fumariaceae*).

This plant is not likely to be confused with any other except species of the same genus, which are very difficult to distinguish among themselves. The genus may be at once recognised by the position of the common stalk of the flowers (peduncle) which is placed opposite to a leaf (leaf-opposed). Attention is also drawn to this same character in the Greater Celandine (figure 76) in the Poppy family, and *Senebiera didyma* (figure 90) in the Crucifer family. Although nectar is secreted in the pouch of the upper petal, the flowers are self-pollinated.

78. Wintercress, *Barbarea vulgaris* R.Br. (× ⅖); perennial, with stiff erect stems up to 2½ ft. high, branched in the upper part; lower stem leaves deeply pinnately divided, the terminal lobe much the largest and more or less obovate or elliptic, the other lobes quite small; stem leaves sessile and markedly eared (auriculate) at the base, more or less deeply lobed or toothed; racemes forming a panicle, the branches of which elongate in fruit; flower-buds (A, × 4) with two short horns at the apex, glabrous; sepals (B, × 3) 4, oblong, obtuse, faintly 3-nerved; petals (C, × 3) 4, narrowly oblanceolate; stamens (D, × 7) 6, 4 long and 2 short; ovary elongated, with a short style; fruits (E, × 1½) very narrow, wavy, more or less erect, about 1 in. long, beaked by the persistent style; seeds (F, × 4) several, very finely and closely pitted (family *Cruciferae*).

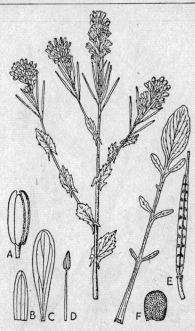

Grows on road-sides, in hedge-banks, and by canals, flowering in spring and summer; a very closely related but less common species is *B. stricta* Andrz., distinguished by its hairy buds.

Wintercress was formerly called Herb St. Barbara, hence the Latin name of the genus. In Sweden it is boiled and eaten.

There is a small fleshy green nectary on each side of the short stamens and these are often united into a semicircular ridge. There is also a larger elongated tooth-like nectary outside and between the bases of each pair of long stamens and corresponding to the short stamens which have disappeared. The latter secrete much less nectar than those at the base of the short stamens.

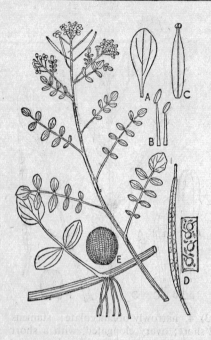

79. Tetraploid Watercress, *Nasturtium microphyllum* Reichb. ($\times \frac{2}{5}$); stem much branched, creeping in mud or floating in shallow water; leaves alternate, pinnate, the end leaflet largest and ovate to orbicular and slightly toothed, the other leaflets gradually smaller downwards, glabrous; flowers small, forming a corymb in the upper part, those of the main shoot maturing first and of the lateral shoots later; sepals 4; petals (A, $\times$ 3) 4, white, broadly spoon-shaped, entire; stamens (B, $\times 3\frac{1}{2}$) 6, 4 long and 2 short; anthers attached near the base; ovary (C, $\times$ 4) soon elongating into fruit, with a short style and 2 stigmas; fruits (D, $\times 1\frac{1}{4}$) nearly 1 in. long; seeds (E, $\times$ 7) globose and finely pitted, the embryonic root lying against the edge of the seed-leaves (cotyledons); (family *Cruciferae*).

Recently Howard and Manton (Ann. Bot. n. ser. 10: 1 (1946)) have shown that two distinct species were confused under the name " Nasturtium officinale R. Br.", the true one, a diploid with short fruits and seeds in a double row, and the other, to be called *N. microphyllum* (see Airy-Shaw, Kew Bull., 1947, 39), a tetraploid with longer fruits and seeds in a single row. My drawing represents the latter.

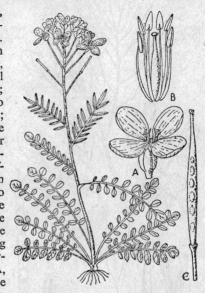

80. Cuckoo Flower, Lady's Smock, *Cardamine pratensis* L. ($\times \frac{2}{5}$); perennial with very short rootstock, often bearing small fleshy scales or tubers; stem erect, up to about 1 ft. high; leaves pinnate, the basal with broader leaflets than those further up the stem; leaflets of basal leaves in 5–7 pairs, elliptic to obovate, the end one larger and more rounded, those of the stem-leaves becoming linear in the uppermost leaves; flowers (A, nat. size) corymbose but cluster slightly, elongating as the lower ones grow into fruits; sepals 4; petals 4, white to mauve; stamens (B, $\times$ 2) 6, 4 long and 2 short, the anthers rather large and attached at the back near the base; ovary elongated, with a short style and head-like stigma; fruit (C, $\times 1\frac{1}{2}$) about 1 in. long, divided into two by a thin partition; seeds in a single row in each loculus (family *Cruciferae*).

This delightful little plant is always a great favourite because it is one of the first to flower in spring, soon following the Primrose. It usually grows in little colonies in moist meadows and by the sides of small streams and brooks. Although little used it may be eaten as a salad in the same way as the ordinary Watercress (fig. 79). There are four nectaries, two larger at the base of the short stamens, and one smaller outside each pair of long stamens. The nectar collects in the pouched bases of the sepals, and the pouches of those opposite the two short stamens with the larger nectaries, are proportionately larger than the other two.

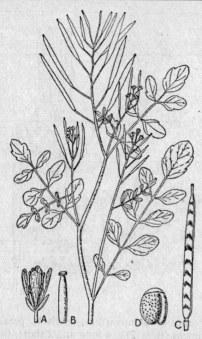

81. Flexuous Bitter-Cress, *Cardamine flexuosa* With. ($\times \frac{2}{5}$); annual, sometimes much branched at the base, glabrous or with a few scattered stiff hairs on the stems and some of the leaves; basal leaves forming more or less a rosette, pinnately lobed into separate pairs of leaflets, these more or less obovate and oblique at the base, the terminal one larger and rounded-obovate; flowers (A, $\times$ 4) very small, in slender axillary and terminal racemes; sepals lanceolate; petals narrow and erect, white; stamens 6, 4 long and 2 short, the longest as long as the petals; anthers small and rounded; ovary (B, $\times$ 6) cylindric, as long as the petals, with a nearly sessile disk-like stigma; fruits (C, $\times$ 1$\frac{1}{2}$) erect, in a slender raceme with a zig-zag (flexuous) axis, $\frac{3}{4}$–1 in. long, undulate with the impression of about a dozen seeds on each face, without nerves; seeds (D, $\times$ 8) compressed, brown, slightly reticulate, with a distinct radical on one side (family *Cruciferae*).

This plant is scarcely recognisable as being related to the much more handsome Cuckoo-flower or Ladies' Smock, *Cardamine pratensis* L., shown in figure 80. It is a much more delicate plant and grows on moist or shady banks, and in waste and cultivated places, and is very widely spread in temperate regions. The name of the species refers to the flexuous or zig-zag growth of the stem and the axis of the raceme, especially when it is in the fruiting stage.

82. Wallflower, *Cheiranthus cheiri* L. ($\times \frac{2}{5}$); perennial with woody stems and several branches, more or less covered on these and the leaves with 2-armed appressed hairs (A, $\times 5$); leaves lanceolate to linear, narrowed to each end, entire; flowers sweet-scented in a lax terminal and sometimes axillary raceme, the lowermost forming fruits whilst the uppermost are still in bud; sepals (B, $\times 2$) 4, narrowly lanceolate; petals (C, $\times 2$) 4, pale yellow to deep red, spoon-shaped, gradually narrowed to the base, veiny; stamens 6, 4 long and 2 short; anthers (D, $\times 1\frac{1}{4}$) rather large, fixed at the base; ovary (E, $\times 3$) covered with short reflexed hairs, with a short stout style, and 2 divergent stigmas; fruit (F, $\times \frac{4}{5}$) narrow, flattened, divided by a thin partition, about $1\frac{1}{2}$–$2\frac{1}{2}$ in. long; grows freely on old walls or rocky railway cuttings, and near houses, either wild or escaped from cultivation; flowers in spring (family *Cruciferae*).

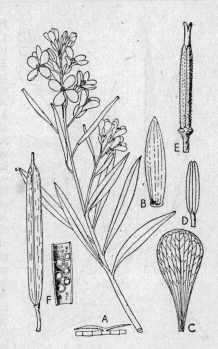

A good spotting feature for this plant when not in flower is the character of the hairy covering on all parts. This is composed of 2-armed hairs with a very short stalk in the middle, the two tips of the arms being free. These peculiar hairs have thus the appearance of lying flat on the surface. There are only two nectaries in the flower, one at the base of each of the two short stamens. The anthers completely close the entrance to the flower. The four upper anthers touch the stigma with their lower ends, while the two lower ones do so with their tips. Either cross-pollination or self-pollination is possible.

83. Charlock, Wild Mustard, *Sinapis arvensis* L. ($\times \frac{2}{5}$); a coarse growing annual weed up to 2 ft. high, often spread amongst corn in great quantity; stems clothed with a few stiff whitish hairs, lower leaves shortly stalked, upper sessile, obovate-elliptic, coarsely toothed or lobulate and toothed, with several spreading forked lateral nerves, with a few stiff hairs mainly on the nerves; flowers yellow, showy, at first in a congested raceme which soon elongates as the fruits develop, some of which are nearly ripe by the time the topmost flowers open; flower-stalks very short; sepals 4, spreading and soon falling off; petals (A, $\times 1\frac{1}{4}$) spoon-shaped with slender claws; stamens 6, 4 long and 2 short; anthers rather large, arrow-shaped at the base; ovary smooth or hairy; fruits (B, $\times \frac{2}{5}$) about 1½ in. long, the upper part composed of a stout beak, the lower part smooth or hispid with reflexed hairs, containing about 10–12 seeds, the latter black and finely pitted-reticulate (family *Cruciferae*).

A common cornfield-weed which when in flower in any quantity gives quite a colour to the landscape. The sepals spread horizontally so that the nectar is exposed, but the flowers are so crowded that insects find it more convenient to reach it in the ordinary way by thrusting their proboscis between the stamens. If cross-pollination is not attained, self-pollination is effected by the stigma pushing up between the anthers.

84. Garlic Mustard, *Alliaria officinalis* Andrz. (flowers and leaves × ⅔; fruits × ⅘); erect annual or biennial up to about 3 ft. high, often crowded together, and when rubbed giving off a strong smell of garlic; stems and leaves glabrous or nearly so; lower leaves on very long stalks, these decreasing in length upwards; leaves broadly ovate-triangular, very widely cordate at the base, triangular-pointed at the apex, very coarsely toothed (dentate); main nerves 3–5 from the base; flowers small

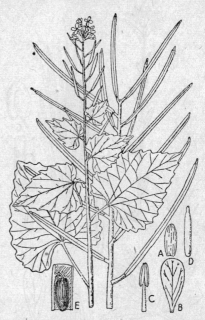

and white, in terminal and lateral racemes though at first forming a close cluster-like corymb; sepals (A, × 2) soon falling off, green, oblong, rounded at the apex, 4–5-nerved; petals (B, × 1⅔) narrowly obovate, white; stamens (C, × 4) 6, 4 long and 2 short; ovary (D, × 3) with a very short bifid style and several ovules; fruits on very short stout spreading stalks, about 2 in. long, nearly cylindrical, very narrow and with a prominent middle nerve on each valve; seeds (E, × 2) with a broad curved stalk, black, oblong-ellipsoid, flattened on one side, lined (striate) lengthwise (synonym *Sisymbrium alliaria* Scop.) (family *Cruciferae*).

This plant grows in colonies under hedges and in shady waste and cultivated places, flowering in spring; easily recognised by the distinctive shape of the leaves, the very short and stout fruit stalks and the striate seeds. The nectaries are placed at the base of the two short stamens, secreting on their inner sides, and filling the space between the filaments and ovary.

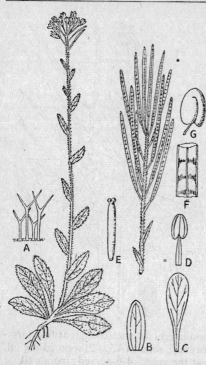

85. Hairy Rockcress, *Arabis hirsuta* (L.) Scop. ($\times \frac{2}{5}$); a stiff, erect biennial or annual with an unbranched stem or rarely with one or two weaker stems in addition, up to about 1 ft. high; basal leaves forming a rosette, spreading, spoon-shaped or oblanceolate, narrowed to a broad-based stalk, entire or with a few teeth, clothed with rather stiff forked hairs (A, $\times$ 15); stem-leaves sessile and half encircling the stem, oblong-lanceolate, rather coarsely toothed only in the lower half or entire; flowers small in a small terminal umbel-like cluster but the axis elongating in fruit; sepals (B, $\times$ 4) 3-nerved; petals (C, $\times$ 4) white, nearly twice as long as the sepals; stamens (D, $\times$ 6) 6, 4 long and 2 shorter; ovary (E, $\times$ 4) elongated, with numerous ovules and a sessile slightly 2-lobed stigma; fruits (F, $\times \frac{2}{5}$) very narrow, erect, with numerous flattened seeds (G, $\times$ 3); flowers in summer and grows on walls, banks and rocks (family *Cruciferae*).

Nectar is secreted only on the inside of the bases of the two short stamens. If cross-pollination is not brought about by insects, self-pollination takes place from the anthers of the longer stamens, which are on the same level or above the stigma. A good spotting feature for this plant is the hairy covering of the leaves which is composed of stiff forked hairs. Similar hairs are found in *Erophila* (fig. 86), and star-shaped hairs in *Capsella* (fig. 87), whilst in the wild Wallflower (fig. 82) they are T-shaped.

86. Whitlow-Grass, *Erophila verna* (L.) E. Mey. ($\times \frac{2}{5}$); dwarf annual flowering in early spring and lasting only a few weeks; leaves all in a dense rosette, and spreading on the ground, oblanceolate to ovate or oblong, slightly toothed, clothed with stalked star-shaped hairs (A, $\times$ 10); flowering stalks (peduncles) several from the leaf-axils, leafless, up to a few inches high, the lower flowers developed into fruits before the uppermost open; flowers very small; sepals (B, $\times$ 10) 4; petals (C, $\times$ 4) 4, white, deeply divided into 2 parts; stamens (D, $\times$ 8) 6, 4 long and 2

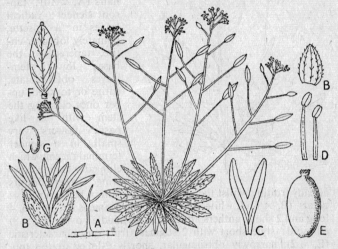

short; anthers attached near the base; ovary (E, $\times$ 5) ellipsoid, with a sessile comb-like stigma; fruits, on long slender stalks, about $\frac{1}{4}$ in. long, compressed, divided by a thin partition, containing numerous minute seeds (G, $\times$ 10) on stalks of varying length (family *Cruciferae*). (In many botanical books this plant is called *Draba verna* L.)

The observer will notice that in this plant and several others nearby (figs. 78 to 89) the stamens are described as being " 4 long and 2 short "; this arrangement is called tetradynamous, and is characteristic of all the Wallflower family *Cruciferae*; other constant features are the four sepals and four petals arranged in the form of a cross, hence the Latin name of the family.

SHEPHERD'S-PURSE, *Capsella bursa-pastoris* (L.) Medik.

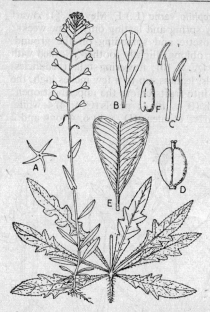

87. Shepherd's-Purse, *Capsella bursa-pastoris* (L.) Medik. (aggregate) (× ⅖); annual, common weed in cultivated and waste places, flowering nearly all the year round, clothed with star-like hairs (A, × 10); tap-root slender; radical leaves in a rosette, pinnately lobed or entire, tapered to the base; lower stem-leaves oblanceolate, entire or toothed, upper ones clasping the stem with ear-like base; flowers very small, in a slender terminal raceme which elongates during flowering; lower flowers already fruiting whilst the uppermost are still in bud; sepals 4; petals (B, × 6) 4, white, spoon-shaped; stamens (C, × 6) 6, 4 long and 2 short, anthers attached in the middle; ovary (D, × 8) ellipsoid; style short with 2 stigmas; fruit very characteristic (E, × 2), narrowly obtriangular, shortly 2-lobed at the top, wedge-shaped to the base; seeds (F, × 5) several in each of the two divisions (family *Cruciferae*).

For our purposes we may regard the Shepherd's Purse as consisting of one rather variable species, though critical students of the British flora are able to recognise more than one. A good spotting character is the star-shaped hairs. It is noteworthy in this highly evolved and most successful type of plant that either cross-pollination or self-pollination may occur, and that the latter is effective. Cultural experiments made in England showed that there was no appreciable difference in the size of plants grown from seed produced by crossing compared with those from self-pollinated stock.

88. Field Penny-Cress, *Thlaspi arvense* L. (× ½); erect glabrous annual up to about 1 ft. or 15 in. high, each branch ending in a raceme of small flowers, most of these becoming almost mature fruit whilst the uppermost are still in bud; lower leaves narrowed to the base but soon withering; upper leaves gradually becoming sessile and earshaped (auriculate) at the base, from oblanceolate (lower ones) to oblong (upper ones), rather

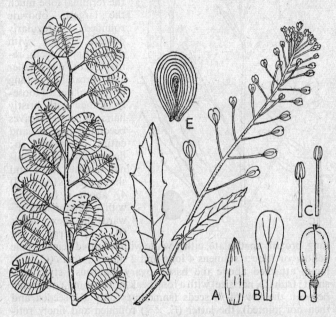

irregularly and distantly toothed (obtusely dentate); flowers more or less corymbose at the top, the axis bearing young fruits soon elongating; sepals (A, × 6) 4, green and faintly 3-nerved; petals (B, × 6) white; stamens (C, × 7) 6, 4 long and 2 a little shorter; ovary (D, × 5) compressed, slightly winged, elliptic, notched at the top and with a very short style; fruits orbicular, thin and flattened contrary to the thin partition between the two halves, not quite the size of a farthing, deeply notched at the top and broadly winged; seeds (E, × 7) 5 or 6 in each loculus, obovoid, dark brown, surrounded by several ribs (family *Cruciferae*).

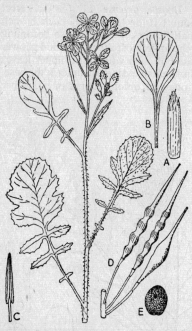

89. Wild Radish, *Raphanus raphanistrum* L. ($\times \frac{2}{5}$); annual or biennial up to 2 ft. high; stems with stiff bristly spreading hairs; leaves deeply pinnately lobed, the terminal lobe much the largest, obovate rounded, irregularly dentate, often with darker tipped teeth, remainder of lobes smaller and spreading, oblong or lanceolate, all loosely clothed with bristly hairs; upper stem-leaves becoming narrow and entire or nearly so; flowers few, in a terminal raceme, large and showy; sepals (A, $\times 1\frac{3}{5}$) 4, about $\frac{1}{8}$ in. long, with a few bristles towards the apex; petals (B, $\times 1\frac{1}{4}$) large, $\frac{3}{4}$ in. long, broadly spathulate, either white with coloured veins or pale yellow or lilac; stamens 4 long and 2 short; anthers (C, $\times 4$) large, attached above the base; ovary glabrous; style very short; fruit (D, nat. size) with a long beak, not opening, contracted between the few (4–7) seeds (sometimes only 1–2-seeded and then not jointed), the latter (E, $\times \frac{3}{5}$) rounded and finely reticulate (family *Cruciferae*).

A common weed of cultivation and waste places, flowering in summer and autumn.

There are four nectaries in the flower, two on the inner side of the short stamens, the other two between the long stamens. Automatic pollination takes place, but is ineffective, the long stamens projecting beyond the stigmas, and the shorter on the same level, the anthers turning their opened sides towards the stigma.

90. Wart Cress, *Coronopus didymus* (L.) Smith ($\times \frac{4}{5}$); annual with numerous spreading or ascending branches, often sprinkled with a few slender hairs; leaves deeply pinnately divided into 3–5 pairs of narrow entire or slightly toothed lobes, glabrous or nearly so; flowers (A, $\times$ 5) very minute, white, arranged in loose leaf-opposed racemes which at first are contracted, but soon elongate in the fruiting stage; stalks slender and soon spreading; sepals 4, boat-shaped; no petals; stamens 2, between the two lobes of the ovary; anthers rounded; ovary

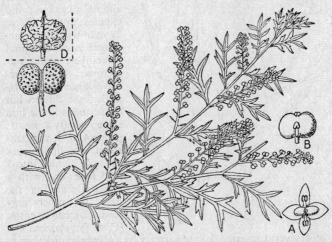

(B, $\times$ 6) 2-lobed, with a sessile minutely 2-lobed stigma in the middle; fruit (C, $\times$ 4) divided into 2 rounded coarsely reticulate lobes readily separating from the central axis (family *Cruciferae*).

This is doubtfully native, but is very common in waste and cultivated ground and spreads rapidly; remarkable in the family in having only 2 stamens instead of the usual 6 with 4 long and 2 short. The second species found in this country, *C. procumbens* Gilib., is really native, and is a coarser plant with shorter racemes of fruits which are not notched at the top, and is coarsely wrinkled and warted, even horned; a sketch of the fruit (D, $\times$ 4) of this species is inset at the top left hand corner of the figure.

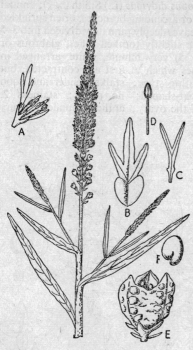

91. Dyer's Mignonette, *Reseda luteola* L. (× $\frac{2}{5}$); biennial or annual, with a hard stiff often unbranched stem; leaves linear to lanceolate, entire but with rather wavy margins, glabrous, pale green or almost glaucous; no stipules; flowers (A, × 2) yellowish green, arranged in stiff terminal spike-like racemes, numerous; bracts narrowly lanceolate, shorter than the flowers but conspicuous in the bud stage; sepals 4, small; petals 4 or 5, very unequal. the upper ones (B, × 5) divided into 3 or 5 lobes and with a 2-lobed scale at the base, the others narrower, 2-lobed or entire (C, × 5); stamens (D, × 4) several, inserted below the ovary on a glandular disk; ovary of 3 carpels, early gaping at the top and exposing the ovules arranged on the walls: fruit (E, × 4) wide open at the top, lobulate around each tiny shining seed (F, × 6); (family *Resedaceae*).

A peculiarity of the genus *Reseda* is that the capsular fruit opens at the top long before the seeds are mature. Even the flower itself is not closed in the bud stage, and it quickly withers. Nectar is secreted at the back of the broad erect disk behind the ovary and the expanded claws of the posterior and middle petals protect it from rain and unwelcome visitors. The plant is common in waste places and grows up to 3 ft. high; employed as a yellow and green dye-plant for cotton and woollen fabrics; similar to and closely related to the Sweet Mignonette of gardens, *Reseda odorata* L.

SWEET VIOLET

Viola odorata

YARROW *Achillea millefolium*

BLACK HOREHOUND *Ballota nigra*

SILVER WEED
Potentilla anserina

BLACKBERRY *Rubus sp.*

HEARTSEASE *Viola tricolor*

MEADOW-SWEET

Filipendula ulmaria

WILD CARROT
Daucus carota

HONEYSUCKLE   *Lonicera periclymenum*

BUTTERBUR   *Petasites hybridus*

WOOD BETONY

Stachys officinalis

92. Chickweed, *Stellaria media* Vill. ($\times \frac{4}{5}$). Annual with succulent smooth stems and branches, except for a line of reflexed hairs along one side; the hairs (F, $\times$ 5) consist of one row of several cells; leaves ovate, the lower hairy on the short stalks; flowers (A, $\times$ 3) scarcely stalked when young, but the stalk elongating in fruit; sepals free and hairy, with a narrow thin border; petals (B, $\times$ 5) shorter than the sepals, deeply 2-lobed, white, usually only one stamen between each, though sometimes the stamens reduced to 3 or 2; anthers pink when young; ovary with 3 styles; fruit (capsule) (D, $\times$ 2½) opening by 6 short teeth; seeds (E, $\times$ 6) several, closely warted, and curved (family *Caryophyllaceae*).

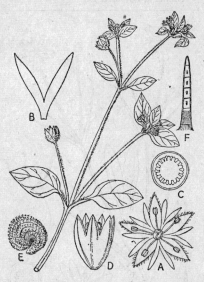

Chickweed is one of the most troublesome weeds in gardens and on farms, and it flowers and produces seed in a very short time. Nevertheless it is of considerable economic and biological interest, representing a high stage of evolution. The seeds provide food for small birds nearly all the year round. There is great economy in the number of the stamens, which are sometimes reduced to 2. A good spotting feature is the line of hairs down one side of the stem, and on the leaf-stalks, and these hairs carry out a special function. They are readily wetted by rain and dew and retain a considerable amount of water. This is conducted down to the leaf-stalks, where some of it is absorbed by the lower cells of the hairs, and any surplus is passed further down to the next pair of leaves and so on; the same process being repeated in each case. One of these hairs is shown enlarged in the figure (F), the three lower cells being absorbent.

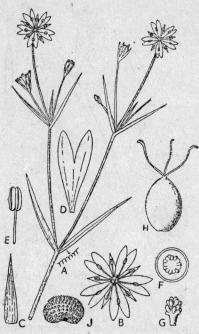

93. Greater Stitchwort, Great Starwort, *Stellaria holostea* L. ($\times \frac{2}{5}$); a perennial with weak stems in hedges and amongst bushes; stems quadrangular, glabrous; leaves sessile, lanceolate to almost linear, tapered to a sharp point, up to about $2\frac{1}{2}$ in. long, with minute comb-like teeth on the margin (A, $\times$ 3); no stipules; flowers (B, $\times \frac{4}{5}$) large, in leafy panicles; stalks slender; sepals (C, $\times 1\frac{1}{2}$) 5, lanceolate, sharply pointed, faintly nerved; petals (D, $\times \frac{4}{5}$) nearly twice as long as the sepals, narrowly wedge-shaped, divided nearly to the middle into 2 divergent lobes; stamens (E, $\times$ 2) 10, nearly as long as the sepals; anthers broadly oblong; ovary (F, $\times$ 5) 1-locular, with the ovules attached to the middle (G, $\times$ 4), ovoid-globose, glabrous, topped by 3 slender styles; fruit a capsule opening by 3 valves; seeds (J, $\times$ 3) kidney-shaped, with transverse lines of warts (family *Caryophyllaceae*).

Compared with the Chickweed (figure 92) this plant has narrow sessile leaves, much larger and more showy flowers and ten stamens; and the stems have not the line of hairs so characteristic of the Chickweed. Three other species of this genus in Britain have the petals considerably longer than the sepals, and only one of these, *S. palustris* Ehrh., is at all common. This has very narrow leaves and the sepals are distinctly 3-nerved.

94. Mouse-Ear Chickweed, *Cerastium vulgatum* L. (aggregate) ($\times \frac{2}{5}$); slender annual; stems with a line of denser hairs down one side; basal leaves stalked, upper opposite, narrowed to the base, narrowly oblanceolate, rather blunt, clothed with rather long hairs, 1-nerved; flowers (A, $\times 1\frac{3}{5}$) in lax cymes, the middle flower already well into fruit, whilst the upper are still opening; pedicels slender; sepals (B, $\times 4$) 5, green with membranous margins, hairy outside; petals (C, $\times 3$) usually longer than the calyx but sometimes shorter or even absent, notched at the apex, white; stamens 10 or 5 or fewer;

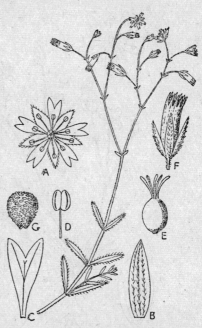

anthers (D, $\times 4$) rounded; ovary (E, $\times 6$) smooth, with 5 free styles; fruit a shining cylindric capsule (F, $\times 1\frac{3}{5}$) opening by 10 sharp narrow teeth, up to twice as long as the calyx; seeds (G, $\times 6$) loosely warted; very variable and sometimes divided by critical botanists into several species; flowers the whole season, usually in cultivated and waste places, etc. (family *Caryophyllaceae*).

Flowers of the Chickweed type of this family have much the same means of pollination. They are usually quite small and inconspicuous and rarely crowded enough to attract much attention. The petals spread out in the sunshine, the nectar secreted at the base of the flower at the same time becoming visible and accessible to insects with a very short proboscis. Flies and the less specialised kinds of bees are the visitors, but automatic self-pollination is usually possible during bad weather.

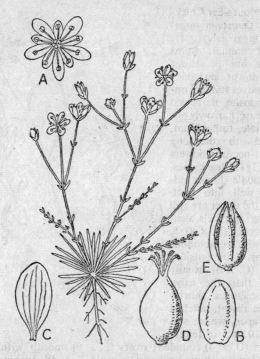

95. Knotted Pearlwort, *Sagina nodosa* (L.) Fenz. ($\times \frac{3}{4}$); a small tufted perennial, often flowering the first year; stems slender, decumbent to erect, thin and wiry, sometimes scarcely branched, glabrous; leaves opposite, the lower linear or needle-like, acute, the upper ones much smaller and mostly with a little cluster of smaller ones in their axils; no stipules; flowers (A, $\times 1\frac{1}{2}$) few, sometimes only one open at the end of each branch or stem; stalks slender; sepals (B, $\times$ 6) 5, broadly elliptic, rounded at the apex, shorter than the 5 narrowly obovate white petals (C $\times 4\frac{1}{2}$); stamens 10; anthers short and rounded; ovary (D, $\times$ 7) smooth, with 5 rather large styles and papillous stigmas, 1-locular with the ovules attached to the central axis; fruit splitting into 5 parts; seeds very minute (family *Caryophyllaceae*).

132

96. Procumbent Pearlwort, *Sagina procumbens* L. (× ¾); a tiny tufted perennial, flowering from the seedling stage; stems short and slender, spreading; leaves in a dense rosette, linear or needle-like, with a very sharp point, smooth or minutely hairy on the margin, the stem leaves opposite and connected by a membranous sheath at the base; no stipules;

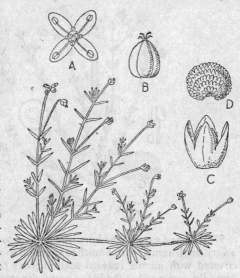

flowers (A, × 3) few, axillary and solitary, and terminal, soon developing into fruit; stalks slender, several times longer than the leaves; sepals 4, broadly elliptic, sometimes tinged with crimson on the margin; petals 4, very small, or absent; stamens 4, opposite the sepals; ovary (B, × 8) ovoid, with 4 short hairy styles, 1-locular, with the ovules attached to the central axis; fruit (C, × 4½) splitting into 4 parts; seeds (D, × 20) very minute (¼ mm.), kidney-shaped, brown, closely pitted; flowers from spring to autumn (family *Caryophyllaceae*).

This little plant has become very much reduced both in stature and in its petals, which are either completely absent or are very minute. Their function has been assumed by the sepals, which are sometimes tinged with crimson on the margin, thus rendering the flower a little more conspicuous. As mentioned under *Anemone*, when one set of organs becomes reduced or dispensed with, another is adapted to perform its function.

There are four small nectaries at the base of the filaments. The stamens are mature at the same time as the stigmas, and automatic self-pollination takes place. The flowers remain closed in dull weather.

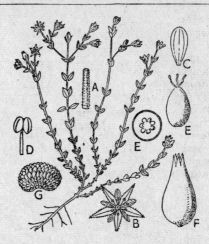

97. Thyme-Leaved Sandwort, *Arenaria serpyllifolia* L. ($\times \frac{2}{5}$);
a very small annual with branched stems up to a few inches long,
covered with minute reflexed scabrid hairs (A, $\times 2\frac{1}{2}$); leaves
opposite, connected at the base around the stem but no stipules,
ovate, acute, loosely covered with very short rough hairs (scabrid)
3–5-nerved from the base; flowers (B, $\times 1\frac{1}{2}$) in the upper leaf-
axils, shortly stalked, very small; sepals 5, larger than the petals,
hairy on the nerves; petals (C, $\times 3$) white, smaller than the
sepals but rather variable in size, obovate; stamens usually 10,
anthers (D, $\times 6$) rounded; ovary (E, $\times 6$) ovoid, smooth, with
3 twisted styles, 1-locular with the ovules arranged around the
central axis (E, $\times 8$); fruit (F, $\times 3$) opening by 6 short teeth at
the top; seeds (G, $\times 6$) kidney-shaped, closely covered with
bead-like warts in transverse rows; often grows on dry walls
and in dry sandy waste places; flowers in summer (family
Caryophyllaceae).

In this species the stamens and stigmas mature simultaneously,
and in bright sunny weather drops of nectar can be seen in the
base of the flower. Sometimes some of the flowers are entirely
female, and even in bisexual flowers the stamens are often reduced
in number. Automatic self-pollination by contact of stigmas and
anthers takes place.

98. Three-Nerved Sandwort, *Arenaria trinervia* L. ($\times \frac{4}{5}$); a delicate, much branched, decumbent or spreading annual up to about 1 ft. long, much resembling the common chickweed (figure 92); stems and branches very slender, with short recurved hairs mainly on one side; leaves opposite, their short stalks connected at the base across the branchlets, ovate or ovate-elliptic, rather abruptly narrowed to the winged stalks, rounded to the shortly acute apex, with 3(–5) distinct parallel nerves from the base to the apex, very minutely hairy on the nerves and margin; flowers (A, $\times$ 2) usually only one from the axil of each pair of leaves, on slender thread-like stalks exceeding the latter in length,

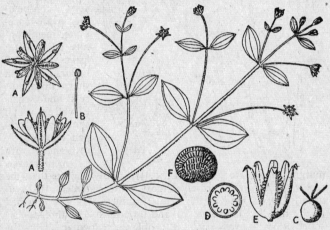

minutely hairy with reflexed hairs; sepals 5, narrow, very acute, with a green minutely hairy keel and white membranous margins; petals white, shorter than the sepals; stamens (B, $\times$ 3) 10, with very slender thread-like filaments, and minute rounded anthers; ovary (C, $\times$ 3) globose, with 3 slender minutely hairy styles, 1-locular, with numerous ovules attached to the central axis (D, $\times$ 5); fruit (E, $\times$ 6) a 6-valved capsule; seeds (F, $\times$ 12) very small (about $\frac{1}{24}$ in.) rounded, rich brown, minutely and transversely grooved, with a white frill-like appendage at the base (family *Caryophyllaceae*).

SAND SPURRY, *Spergularia campestris* (All.) Aschers.

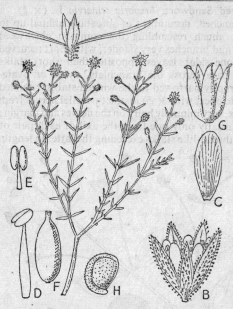

99. Sand Spurry, *Spergularia campestris* (All.) Aschers. ($\times \frac{3}{4}$); small annual or biennial with numerous stems branching from the base and forming flat tufts; stipules (A, $\times 4\frac{1}{2}$) very conspicuous, ovate-lanceolate, membranous and white; leaves opposite, linear, with a sharp tip; pedicels and sepals clothed with short gland-tipped hairs (B, $\times$ 6); sepals with a membranous margin, lanceolate; petals (C, $\times 4\frac{1}{2}$) usually shorter than the sepals, usually pink, rarely almost white; stamens (D, $\times$ 9) usually 10, as long as the petals; anthers (E, $\times$ 9) attached in the middle; filaments flat and broad; style with 3–5 very short lobes; ovary (F, $\times$ 10) oblong, 1-locular, with the ovules attached to the central axis; fruit (G, $\times$ 4) opening in as many valves as styles (3–5); seeds (H, $\times$ 15) with the rootlet (radicle) conspicuous on one side, minutely warted (family *Caryophyllaceae*).

Grows in sandy or gravelly heaths and waste places, and very widely distributed in the northern hemisphere and even in Australia. A coastal form is often treated as a species, *Spergularia sabina* Presl (synonym *S. marina* Griseb.). This, as is often the case with maritime forms of species, has thicker more fleshy leaves.

Frequently only three stamens are developed. Nectar is secreted by a fleshy ring inside the base of the stamens. In bad weather the flowers remain closed and automatic self-pollination then takes place.

RAGGED ROBIN, *Lychnis flos-cuculi* L.

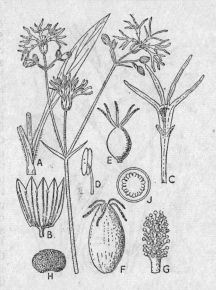

100. Ragged Robin, *Lychnis flos-cuculi* L. ($\times \frac{2}{5}$); perennial with erect rather weak stems and long internodes; leaves opposite, narrowly linear-oblanceolate, fringed with hairs towards the base (A, $\times \frac{4}{5}$); flowers in loose terminal clusters (cymes) the middle flower the oldest and often forming the fruit whilst the others are still open or in bud; calyx (B, $\times 1\frac{1}{4}$) shortly 5-lobed and with 10 conspicuous ribs; petals (C, $\times 1\frac{1}{4}$) 5, red, deeply cut into 4 linear lobes, the middle pair longest, the claw with two appendages near the middle; stamens (D, $\times$ 3) 10, the 5 outer maturing first and then curving outwards, making room for the 5 inner; the 5 styles mature last of all, their ends being spirally twisted; pollination by insects, the nectar secreted at the base of the stamens; ovary (E, $\times$ 2) 1-locular, with the ovules on the central axis; capsule (F, $\times$ 2) ellipsoid, opening by 5 teeth, the styles often remaining; seeds (G, $\times 1\frac{1}{2}$) stalked on the axis, kidney-shaped, closely warted (H, $\times$ 3) (J, cross section of ovary, $\times 2\frac{1}{2}$) (family *Caryophyllaceae*).

In this species nectar is secreted at the base of the stamens, which open before the stigmas are receptive to pollen. The five outer stamens are mature first, and their anthers as they open occupy the middle of the flower; after their pollen is shed, their filaments elongate and curve outwards, making room for the inner five stamens, which in turn follow the same procedure. Then the five styles develop and occupy the same position in the middle of the flower.

101. Corn Cockle, *Lychnis githago* (L.) Scop. ($\times \frac{1}{2}$); a tall coarse annual clothed all over with long silky hairs and scabrid below these; leaves opposite, linear, sessile, with a prominent midrib; flowers scentless, solitary on long nude stalks thickening towards the top; calyx-lobes longer than the petals, the tube strongly ribbed outside; petals (A, $\times \frac{4}{5}$) spreading, red, widely notched at the apex; stamens 10, in two series; anthers (B, $\times 1\frac{1}{2}$) arrow-shaped; styles 5, free to the base; ovary (C, nat. size) 1-locular, with the ovules attached to the middle; capsule (E, $\times \frac{4}{5}$) opening by 5 teeth at the top, surrounded by the enlarged calyx; seeds (F, $\times 3$) obovoid, closely warted (D, cross-section of ovary, $\times 1\frac{1}{2}$) (family *Caryophyllaceae*).

Some botanists on the continent of Europe treat this cornfield weed as a separate genus, *Agrostemma*. The differences are not very pronounced, however, though this is a very striking plant with its long pointed calyx-lobes. The stamens and stigmas mature in turn, and pollination is by butterflies. The flowers appear in July and August, and remain open at night and during bad weather.

The roughness of the seed-coat serves to fix it in the soil. The seeds are poisonous and dangerous if mixed with cereals. They give a disagreeable odour to bread and render it unfit for human consumption.

102. Red Campion, *Lychnis dioica* L. ($\times \frac{2}{3}$); biennial up to
2 ft. high; stems covered with long spreading and shorter slightly
reflexed hairs, not sticky; leaves opposite, subsessile, ovate,
rounded to an acute apex, pubescent with short stiff hairs above
and on the nerves beneath, more or less 3-nerved from above
the base, the younger ones often tinged with dull crimson; no
stipules; flowers unisexual (dioecious), the males on one, the

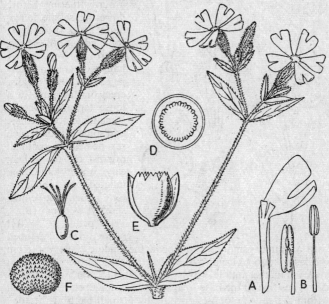

females on another plant, few together; stalks about $\frac{1}{2}$-in. long;
calyx tubular, about $\frac{3}{4}$-in. long, 5-toothed at the apex, prominently 5-ribbed, and with 5 less prominent ribs, pubescent,
crimson-green; petals (A, $\times 1\frac{3}{4}$) 5, deep pink, 2-lobed with a long
pale claw and 2 toothed white outgrowths at the top; stamens
(B, $\times 2\frac{1}{2}$) 10, the longest opening first; anthers large, dull white;
ovary (C, $\times 3$) ellipsoid, 1-locular, with numerous ovules on the
central placenta (D, $\times 8$); styles 5; fruit (E, $\times 2$) contained in
the bladder-like expanded calyx, campanulate, opening at the top
by 10 short teeth; seeds (F, $\times 10$) numerous, kidney-shaped,
closely warted (family *Caryophyllaceae*).

139

BLADDER CAMPION, *Silene cucubalus* Wibel

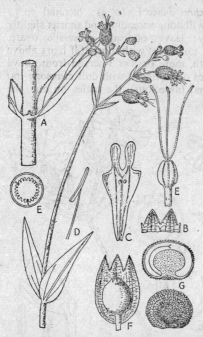

103. Bladder Campion, *Silene cucubalus* Wibel ($\times \frac{2}{5}$); perennial branched from the base; stems glabrous or rarely pubescent; leaves (A, $\times 1\frac{1}{2}$) opposite, the lower withering before flowering, sessile, lanceolate, acute at the apex, rounded at the base, glabrous or very shortly hairy, margins minutely jagged; flowers few, erect or drooping, in a loose terminal cluster, some male, some female and some bisexual, each sex possessing vestigial organs of the other; calyx about $\frac{1}{2}$ in. long, inflated and bladderlike, much net-veined, shortly 5-lobed (B, $\times 1\frac{1}{4}$); petals (C, $\times 1\frac{1}{3}$) white, deeply 2-lobed with a pair of small scales above the middle, 3-nerved from the base; stamens usually 10, with rather large anthers (D, $\times 1\frac{1}{3}$) attached in the middle; ovary (E, $\times \frac{3}{4}$) 3-locular, with 3 slender styles free to the base; capsule (F, nat. size) shortly stalked within the calyx, globose, opening by 6 small teeth at the top; seeds (G, $\times 6$) kidney-shaped, closely covered with warts (family *Caryophyllaceae*).

Insect visitors are mainly moths and humble-bees, the nectar being concealed at a depth of nearly half an inch. Humble-bees often steal the nectar by perforating the calyx instead of by the ordinary entrance between the deeply 2-lobed petals. Another name for this species is *Silene inflata* Smith.

104. Soapwort, *Saponaria officinalis* L. (× ⅖); perennial with several rather stout leafy stems up to 2 ft. high; stems glabrous; leaves opposite, connected at the base across the stem by a marked rim, ovate-lanceolate to lanceolate, gradually merging into bracts in the upper parts, strongly marked with 3-5 parallel nerves from the base, narrowed to the apex, very slightly roughened on the margins, but otherwise glabrous; no stipules; flowers large and handsome, arranged in a series of small cymes with leafy bracts, the ultimate stalks very short; a pair of narrow bracts just below each flower; calyx tubular, 5-lobed, the lobes in bud forming a narrow beak; petals (A, × ⅖) pale pink or nearly white, free, with a long claw and a broad blade notched at the top, the claw with a 2-toothed scale on the inside; stamens (C, × ⅘) 10, well exserted from the petals; ovary (B, × 3) glabrous, with only 2 styles, 1-locular, with numerous ovules arranged on the central axis; capsule (D, × 2) opening at the top by 4 teeth (family *Caryophyllaceae*).

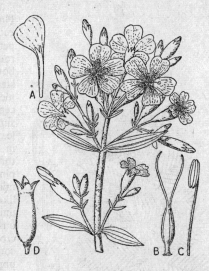

To be found in flower in summer on banks, roadsides and waste places, and it ranges far into western Asia; common around villages and probably only native in south-west England. It is easily recognised among British members of the family by the two styles. The fragrant odour of the flowers becomes much stronger in the evening, and hawk-moths are the chief pollinating agents, the nectar being secreted at the bottom of the calyx-tube. Double-flowered forms sometimes occur. As indicated by its common name, the plant was formerly used as soap, the leaves being boiled and macerated for the purpose.

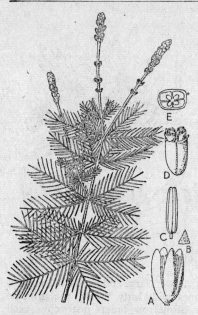

105. Spicate Water-Milfoil, *Myriophyllum spicatum* L. ($\times \frac{2}{5}$); aquatic perennial with a creeping rootstock rooting at the bottom of the water; stems usually wholly immersed in the water except the flowering spikes, simple or branched; leaves whorled, usually in fours, distributed throughout the stem, pinnately divided to the midrib into fine thread-like segments; flowers unisexual and monoecious, the males (A, $\times$ 4) crowded and forming a continuous spike in the upper part, the females (D, $\times$ 6) spaced at intervals in whorls of four, each subtended by a small ovate toothed bract; male flowers with 4 conspicuous crimson sepals covering the six stamens; petals (B, $\times$ 8) very small and triangular, toothed; anthers (C, $\times$ 6) large, on short filaments attached at the base; no rudimentary ovary; female flowers (D, $\times$ 6) with the 4-grooved calyx adnate to the 4-locular ovary (E, $\times$ 6) and without lobes, with microscopic triangular petals between; stigmas 4, short and broad, with a broad brush-like top; fruit a globose or oblong capsule, each lobe separating into 1-seeded parts (family *Halorrhagaceae*).

This plant grows in water in ditches and ponds and flowers most of the summer. The flowers are wind-pollinated, the anthers being large and containing abundant easily dispersed pollen, which is blown on to the stigmas, already well developed and receptive before the anthers open. The second British species, *M. verticillatum* L., is less common, and its flowers do not appear above the water, except when very shallow, but the bracts or floral leaves are then longer than the flowers.

106. Water Purslane, *Peplis portula* L. ($\times \frac{2}{5}$); a creeping sometimes much-branched annual often forming wide patches in ditches and moist places, rooting at the lower nodes; stems glabrous, green or tinged with crimson; leaves opposite, shortly stalked, spoon-shaped, gradually narrowed to the base, rounded at the apex, glabrous, with 2-3 pairs of lateral spreading nerves; no stipules; flowers (A, $\times$ 6) very small in the axils of the leaves, scarcely stalked; calyx (B, $\times$ 8) widely bell-shaped, with 6 acutely triangular inner lobes and 6 awl-shaped outer lobes between; petals very minute and pink or often absent; stamens 6, inserted outside a thin nectar-secreting ring around the base of the ovary (C, $\times$ 8); style very short, with 2 rounded stigmas;

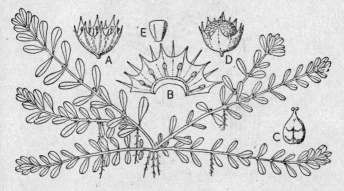

fruit (D, $\times$ 4) a depressed-globose capsule girt by the calyx, with a very thin coat showing the shape of the numerous small broadly obovoid slightly angular seeds (E, $\times$ 8).

When growing partly in water, submerged flowers remain closed, and, since they contain air, are automatically self-pollinated. When mature in the open air the flowers are wide open and the six stamens are curved inwards, so that automatic self-pollination is also inevitable, especially when the flowers close and the anthers press against the stigma. Fruits are produced in great abundance.

The Water Purslane belongs to the family *Lythraceae*, which is very poorly represented in Britain, there being only three species, the one here shown, the handsome Purple Loosestrife shown on the next page, and the Hyssop, *Lythrum hyssopifolium* L., which has the upper leaves linear and alternate.

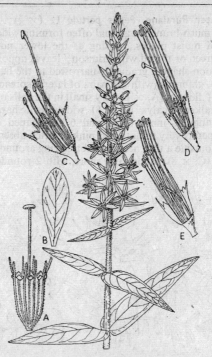

107. Purple Loosestrife, *Lythrum salicaria* L. (× ½); perennial; stems erect, up to 3 ft. high, rather densely leafy, hairy;
leaves opposite or 3 in a whorl, sessile and clasping the stem,
lanceolate, rounded at the base, gradually acute at the apex,
shortly hairy below, with prominently looped lateral nerves;
flowers arranged in a dense terminal spike-like raceme leafy
towards the base with smaller green leafy bracts throughout;
calyx (A, × 3) tubular, usually with 6–8 short triangular lobes
and as many subulate teeth between them; petals (B, × 2½)
often 6, inserted at the top of the calyx tube, reddish purple or
pink with darker veins, oblanceolate; stamens about twice as
many as the petals (see note p. 145); ovary free within the calyx-
tube, 2-locular; stigma head-like (capitate); fruit a capsule with
several seeds; grows in wet ditches and by sides of ponds, rivers,
etc., flowering during summer (family *Lythraceae*).

Darwin investigated very thoroughly the structure and function of the flowers of this species, which are of three forms (trimorphic), differing in the comparative length of the stamens and styles; this arrangement is of benefit to the species, because the reproductive organs, when of different length, behave to one another like different species of the same genus in regard to productiveness and character of the offspring. The diagrams in the sketch opposite show these different forms of flowers :

C, *long-styled flowers* : style longer than the stamens; half of the latter are of medium length, half short.

D, *medium-styled flowers* : style of medium length; half of the stamens longer than the style, half short.

E, *short-styled flowers* : style short; half of the stamens long and the other half of medium length.

The anthers of the long stamens are green, and produce the largest pollen grains; the medium length and the short stamens are yellow, and have medium-sized and small pollen respectively. There are eighteen possible modes of pollination in this arrangement, but Darwin showed that only six lead to complete fertility, in which each length of style bearing the stigma receives pollen from anthers situated at a corresponding level. This is brought about by insects which visit the flower for the nectar secreted in the fleshy base of the calyx. The red inner surface of the calyx and the dark veins of the petals which point to the middle of the flower serve as guides to the nectar.

The most noteworthy visitor is a bee which sucks the nectar and gathers the pollen, and almost confines itself to this plant when it is in flower. When it thrusts into the calyx-tube it touches the shortest set of reproductive organs with the undersurface of its head, the next set with the ventral surface of its thorax, and the longest set with the ventral surface of its abdomen, the dimensions of the insect exactly suiting the flower.

108. Rose-Bay, *Epilobium angustifolium* L. ($\times \frac{1}{2}$); a very beautiful plant, but in some parts a troublesome weed; stems reddish, usually unbranched, up to about 4 ft. high, the base of the leaf forming a ridge for a short distance below the base, glabrous or minutely hairy; leaves numerous, ascending, narrowly lanceolate to almost linear, tapered at both ends, up to about 6 in. long, entire or with very minute and distant teeth, with very numerous nerves spreading at a right angle, looped and forming a wavy line well within the margin; flowers (A, $\times$ $1\frac{1}{2}$, petals removed) arranged in a very showy terminal raceme up to about a foot or more long; upper leaves gradually transformed into narrow bracts below each flower; flower-stalks up to $\frac{1}{2}$ in. long, hoary like the ovary and calyx above with very short mealy hairs; calyx above the ovary, with a little hump at the top in bud, lobes 4, spreading, lanceolate, $\frac{1}{2}$ in. long; petals (B, $\times$ 2) 4, spreading, purplish red, obovate, narrowed into a slender claw, slightly notched at the top, veiny; stamens 8, nearly as long as the petals; anthers rather large, fixed to the back above the base; ovary inferior, 4-locular, long and narrow; style shorter than the stamens, with a deeply 4-lobed stigma; fruit (C, nat. size) about 2 in. long, splitting into 4 narrow divisions and releasing the very numerous tiny seeds (D, $\times$ 4) clothed at one end with a tuft of long slender white hairs by means of which they float away in the wind (family *Onagraceae*).

This is one of our most beautiful wild plants which flowers in summer and grows chiefly in light soil in moist open woods. The flowers open between 6 and 7 a.m., and the anthers are mature before the stigmas (protandrous), thus preventing self-pollination. The nectar is secreted by the fleshy green top of the ovary, and is protected from rain by the expanded bases of the filaments and hairs on the style just above them. In freshly-opened flowers the stamens serve as a landing place for insects, for the style is still short and the stigmas not receptive. The pollen grains, which are bound together by threads of viscin, are thus carried to another and older flower in which the stamens have curved downwards, and their place taken by the elongated style with its four spreading stigmas which in turn provide the only alighting place.

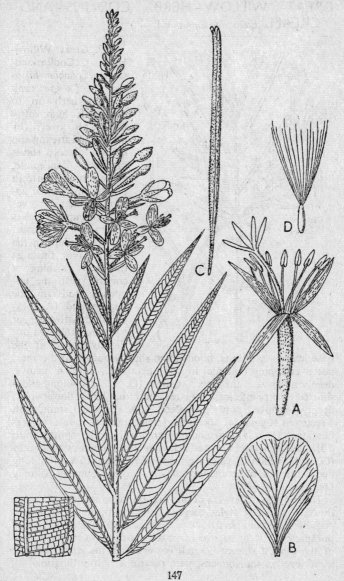

109. Great Willow-Herb, Codlins-and-Cream, *Epilobium hirsutum* L. ($\times \frac{2}{5}$); rank growing herb up to about 5 ft. high, softly hairy all over, by ditches and streams and in wet places; leaves opposite, lanceolate, acute, toothed, the teeth pointed and curved upwards; lateral nerves several; upper leaves becoming alternate; flowers axillary in the upper leaves, those at the top forming a corymb with the un-opened buds in the middle; buds (A, $\times 1\frac{1}{2}$) ellipsoid, with 4 slender tips; sepals (B, $\times 1\frac{1}{4}$) 4, slightly united at the base, narrowly oblong, hooded and shortly horned at the apex, not overlapping (valvate) in bud; petals (C, $\times 1\frac{1}{4}$) 4, mauve, deeply notched at the apex; stamens (D, $\times 2\frac{1}{2}$) 8, 4 long and 4 shorter; ovary inferior, elongated and rather like a flower-stalk, deeply 4-grooved, softly pubescent; style (E, $\times 2\frac{1}{2}$) stout, with 4 recurved stigmas far above the longer stamens; ovules numerous; fruit (F, $\times \frac{2}{5}$) long and slender, quadrangular, splitting into 4 slender recurved parts and releasing the numerous tiny seeds (G, $\times 1\frac{1}{2}$) which float away in the wind by means of a tuft of long fine white hairs at the top; flowers during summer (family *Onagraceae*).

Three types of flowers occur, but on separate plants; large flowers with long styles curved so that self-pollination is not possible; medium-sized flowers, with a straight style, and if cross-pollination fails the stigmas curve back so as to touch the anthers of the longest stamens; small flowers with the stigmas at the same level as the stamens, with inevitable self-pollination.

110. Enchanter's Nightshade, *Circaea lutetiana* L. (× ⅖); perennial herb with a slender creeping rootstock; stems annual, up to about 2 ft. high, clothed with very short whitish hairs; leaves opposite, stalked, ovate, rounded or slightly heart-shaped (cordate) at the base, rather broadly pointed at the apex, the few pairs of lateral nerves forming a distinct loop well within the margin, shortly toothed on the margin and very thin, slightly hairy below to glabrous, the stalk and midrib sometimes suffused with crimson; flowers (A, × 2) in slen-

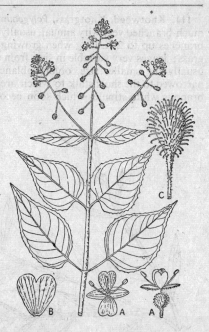

der terminal and axillary racemes, sometimes these 3 together at the top, each flower becoming pendulous in opening; stalks slender; sepals 2, crimson, soon reflexed, inserted at the top of a short stalk on top of the inferior ovary; petals (B, × 4) 2, white or pink, deeply notched; stamens 2, opposite the sepals; ovary inferior, covered with hooked hairs; style with a 2-lobed stigma, girt at the base by a ring of nectar; fruits (C, × 4) with deflexed stalks, club-shaped, covered with slender hooked bristles, containing 2 seeds; flowers during the summer and grows in woods and shady places, often in great abundance, but rare in Scotland, where, however, there is another species, *C. alpina* L., a much smaller plant and the fruit with usually only one seed; cross-pollination is brought about by hover flies which cling to the stamens and stigmas (family *Onagraceae*).

The hooked, slender bristles on the fruits account for the wide distribution of this plant, as they cling to the fur of animals.

111. Knotweed, Knotgrass, *Polygonum aviculare* L. ($\times \frac{1}{2}$); a much-branched very wiry annual, usually prostrate, with stems or branches up to 2 ft. long when growing amongst crops or long grass; leaves very variable in size, from about $\frac{1}{3}$ in. to $1\frac{1}{2}$ in. but usually the smaller size, oblong-oblanceolate to oblanceolate, narrowed to the short stalk to which are adnate the large membranous white stipules which soon become split and jagged on

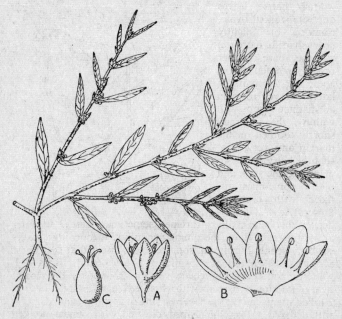

the margins; flowers (A, $\times$ 5) bisexual, axillary, shortly stalked, few together, pinkish; sepals (B, $\times$ 7) 5, connate at the base overlapping in bud; stamens 8, five alternating with the sepals; ovary (C, $\times$ 6) with 3 styles; fruits surrounded by the persistent calyx-lobes which have whitish margins, triangular, beaked, very minutely pitted-reticulate (family *Polygonaceae*).

A troublesome weed which flowers and fruits nearly the whole season. It seems to thrive best where most trampled upon and ill-treated.

112. Sheep's Sorrel, *Rumex acetosella* L. ($\times \frac{2}{5}$); a very acid slender perennial plant; stems reddish or green and red; leaves alternate, stalked, narrowly lanceolate to oblanceolate, entire except for two spreading lobes (auricles) near the base, covered with minute wart-like protuberances; stalks usually shorter than the leaf-blade; stipules conspicuous, membranous, soon splitting up into segments; flowers very small, unisexual or sometimes bisexual, the males (A, $\times$ 3) usually on one plant, the females on another (dioecious), arranged in slender lax terminal panicles, the pedicels in little clusters, those of the male very slender; bracts membranous; sepals small, obovate or elliptic, glabrous; no petals; stamens (B, $\times$ 6) (in the male) 6, with rather large anthers and very short filaments; female flowers with shorter stalks than the male; ovary (C, $\times$ 3) globose, with 3 deeply lobed fringe-like stigmas; nut (D, $\times$ 4) enclosed by the inner sepals which do not become enlarged as in the closely related species *R. acetosa* L., and the outer sepals remain erect, not reflexed as in the latter (family *Polygonaceae*).

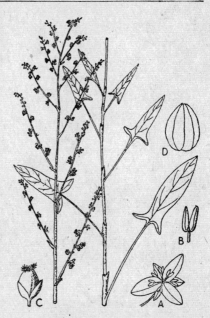

The flowers of this species are very small and are wind-pollinated, though sometimes visited by insects, the pollen being caught by the fringe-like stigmas. It is often a very troublesome weed and difficult to eradicate. As it contains oxalic acid it has been known to cause poisoning in stock.

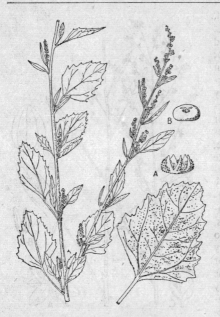

113. Goosefoot, Fat Hen, *Chenopodium album* L. (× ⅖) an annual up to 2 ft. high, pale green or mealy white, especially the flowers and lower surfaces of the leaves; leaves alternate, stalked, the lowermost more or less triangular or almost rhomboid, and bluntly and coarsely toothed, gradually becoming narrower upwards to almost linear and entire, distinctly 3-nerved near the base; often completely covered below by rounded whitish papillae; flowers (A, × 3) bisexual, arranged in short dense axillary spikes and forming a leafy spike-like panicle at the top of the shoot; calyx of 5 equal rounded lobes; no petals; stamens usually 5; ovary (B, × 4) depressed; styles mostly 3; fruit depressed-globose; blackish, more or less covered by the persistent calyx lobes; seeds spreading horizontally, black, rounded-kidney-shaped, with the embryo forming almost a ring around the endosperm (family *Chenopodiaceae*).

This is an abundant annual weed to be found on most rubbish heaps. It multiplies rapidly by seed and spreads very quickly. Formerly this plant was used as a potherb and boiled and eaten like spinach, by which it has been replaced. The leaves are sometimes completely covered below by a rounded mealy substance, which makes the plant easy to recognise.

114. Common Orache, *Atriplex patula* L. (aggregate) (× ½); annual, very variable in size and leaf-shape, usually branched from the base, rather similar to *Chenopodium album* (figure 113), but the lower leaves mostly opposite; leaves stalked, the lower larger and more or less triangular with two spreading lobes (hastate) towards the base, the upper becoming much narrower and sometimes entire or coarsely toothed, glabrous or minutely mealy-papillous; flowers unisexual, the male (A, × 2) and female (B, × 2) on the same plant (monoecious), arranged in

slender leafy spikes forming a terminal panicle, the females usually mixed with the males, mostly covered with mealy papillae; male flowers with 5 ovate-triangular entire sepals, and 5 stamens opposite to them; female flower consisting of two herbaceous toothed bracts which enlarge in fruit, the latter (C, × 3½) slightly compressed, black and hard (family *Chenopodiaceae*).

Very similar in general appearance to the *Chenopodium* in figure 113, but usually less mealy, and always to be distinguished in the fruiting stage. The fruits are little hard rounded structures and are enclosed in two closely appressed toothed bracts which make the clusters look rather prickly. Like the *Chenopodium* it is common in cultivated and waste ground.

153

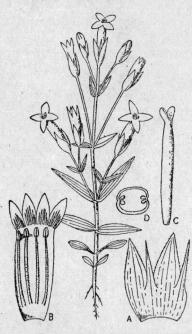

115. Field Gentian, *Gentiana campestris* L. ($\times \frac{2}{5}$); erect annual up to about 9 inches high with a slender tap-root; leaves opposite, gradually increasing in size upwards, sessile, the largest about 1 inch long and broadly lanceolate, prominently 3-nerved from the base, minutely papillous on the margin; flowers axillary and solitary or on short axillary branches; stalks up to $1\frac{1}{2}$ in. long; calyx (A, $\times 1\frac{1}{4}$) leaf-like, 4-lobed to about the middle, the two outer lobes ovate-lanceolate, much broader than the two inner linear sharp-pointed lobes, all minutely papillous on the margin; corolla (B, $\times 1\frac{3}{4}$) pale blue, twice as long as the calyx, 4-lobed, fringed with long blue hairs at the mouth; stamens 4, alternate with the corolla-lobes, and inserted well down the tube; anthers facing inwards; ovary (C, $\times 2$) nearly as long as the stamens, 1-locular, with the numerous ovules arranged on two placentas along the walls (D, $\times 6$); stigma deeply 2-lobed; fruit a capsule with numerous rounded seeds; flowers in late summer and autumn; in pastures and on commons mostly in limestone districts (family *Gentianaceae*).

Nectar is secreted at the bottom of the corolla and can only be reached by humble bees and *Lepidoptera* because of the dense fringe of bristly hairs at the mouth of the corolla. This is the most common of the nine species of Gentian accredited to the British flora, and it is not likely to be mistaken for any except *Gentiana amarella* L. (fig. 116), which has 5 corolla-lobes, and 5 calyx-lobes all narrowly lanceolate, and of equal size.

116. Autumn Gentian, *Gentiana amarella* L. (× ⅖), erect, simple or branched annual, with stiff erect branches, sometimes only a few inches high or up to 15 inches and then very slender; stems often tinged with crimson or purple, glabrous; leaves opposite, sessile, lanceolate to narrowly ovate, rounded and clasping the stem at the base, apex obtuse to somewhat acute, more or less 3-nerved from the base, entire; flowers few to numerous and crowded, sometimes so numerous as to form a leafy panicle; stalks variable, but up to ¾ inch; long in fruit; calyx (A, × 1½) divided to the middle into 5 equal acute narrow lobes; corolla (B,

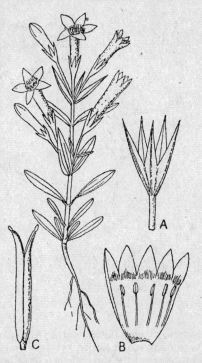

× ⅘) pale purplish-blue, 2–2½ times as long as the calyx; lobes 5, with a dense fringe of erect stiff hairs within the mouth; stamens 5, alternate with the corolla-lobes; ovary 1-locular, with 2 rows of ovules on the walls; stigmas nearly sessile, broad, remaining on the capsule (C, × ⅘) like a little tongue, the capsule about ½ in. long and splitting down the middle; seeds numerous, rounded, brown and very minutely pitted (family *Gentianaceae*).

This species is more common in some localities (dry hilly pastures, cliffs and dunes), but not so widely distributed as *Gentiana campestris* L. (fig. 115). In *G. amarella* there are 5 calyx-lobes, all narrow and equal in size and shape. In *G. campestris*, however, there is a reduction to 4 calyx-lobes, and these are unequal in size and shape, two of them being broadly ovate and overlapping, the other two much narrower ones.

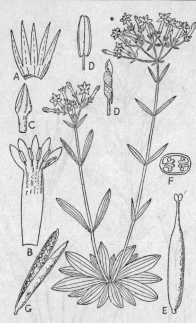

117. Centaury, *Centaurium umbellatum* Gilib. ($\times \frac{2}{5}$); erect annual, varying much in size according to situation from an inch up to a foot high, usually much-branched from the base; stems and branches narrowly ribbed, glabrous; leaves opposite, often forming also a basal rosette, these spoon-shaped-oblanceolate and prominently 3-nerved from the base; stem leaves sessile, lanceolate to almost linear, with 3-parallel nerves; flowers numerous in a rather dense repeatedly forked cyme, the middle flower of each branch nearly sessile; bracts paired below each lateral flower; calyx (A, $\times$ 2) deeply 5-lobed, the lobes very narrow and keeled; corolla pink, tube cylindric, narrow, contracted at the top and then spreading into a 5-lobed limb (B, $\times$5); lobes twisted in bud (C, $\times$ 1$\frac{1}{4}$); stamens (D, $\times$ 5) 5, the anthers large and exserted from the tube, with a short slender 2-lobed style as high as the anthers, and with two placentas (F, $\times$ 5) projecting into the middle; ovules numerous on the two placentas; capsule (G, $\times$ 2) splitting along the placentas, with numerous seeds; grows in dry pastures, sandy banks and by roadsides, flowering all the summer (family *Gentianaceae*).

A striking feature is the spiral twisting of the anthers after opening. The stigma is mature when the flower opens, and the anthers discharge their pollen in succession, at which time the style is bent away to one side, whilst the stamens bend to the other side, when cross-pollination may take place. Later the stigma and anthers become erect and self-pollination is possible.

118. Buckbean, *Menyanthes trifoliata* L. ($\times \frac{2}{5}$); herb growing in water, with a creeping rootstock and dense mat of roots; stem rather thick, creeping or floating, covered by the large sheathing bases of the leaves, the latter alternate, divided into 3 separate obovate leaflets rounded at the apex and with a few ascending looped lateral nerves; sheathing base up to about 2 in. long, membranous; flowers several in a raceme on a long stalk arising from below the tuft of leaves, each flower with a bract at the base shorter than its own stalk, the latter up to about 1 inch long; calyx deeply 5-lobed, lobes oblong, rounded at the apex; corolla (A, $\times 1\frac{1}{2}$) broadly tubular, 5-lobed, lobes not overlapping in bud (valvate), densely clothed on the inside with numerous white hairs; stamens (B, $\times 2\frac{1}{4}$) 5, alternate with the corolla-lobes; ovary (C, $\times 2\frac{1}{4}$) with only 1 loculus and ovules arranged on the walls; fruit (D, E $\times 1\frac{1}{5}$) a capsule bursting into 2 parts; seeds (F, $\times 2\frac{1}{4}$) few, rounded, slightly compressed, light brown and shining, $\frac{1}{8}$ in. diam. (family *Menyanthaceae*).

This plant is usually classified with the Gentians (*Gentianaceae*), but there are good reasons for treating it as a distinct family. In the Gentian family the leaves are always opposite and the corolla-lobes overlap and are twisted in bud, whilst in the Buckbean, and its related genus *Limnanthemum*, the leaves are alternate and the corolla-lobes do not overlap or twist in bud. The flowers of the Buckbean are mostly of two kinds, a long-styled and a short-styled form, with a corresponding position for the anthers.

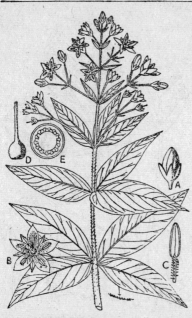

119. Yellow Loosestrife, *Lysimachia vulgaris* L. (× ⅖); perennial with erect stems up to about 3 ft. high, growing on shady banks near water; leaves in whorls, the lower 4 or 3 in a whorl, the upper mostly in pairs, broadly to narrowly lanceolate, very shortly stalked at the base, gradually tapered to the apex, slightly pubescent below, with entire or undulate minutely jagged margins; flowers (B, × ⅔) in leafy terminal panicles; stalks slender, pubescent, with small narrow bracts at their base; sepals 5, broadly lanceolate, fringed with very short hairs; corolla yellow with a short broad tube, 5-lobed, the lobes (A, × 2) twisted (contorted) in bud, densely covered above by short glandular hairs; stamens (C, × 2½) 5, opposite the corolla-lobes, with rudiments of filaments between; anthers large; filaments covered with short gland-tipped hairs; ovary (D, × 2½) globose, 1-locular, with numerous ovules arranged on the central basal placenta (E, × 7); fruit a capsule (family *Primulaceae*). There are no nectaries in the flowers, but the abundant pollen in the very large anthers is collected by certain bees which carry it in balls on their hind legs.

The family *Primulaceae* is quite well represented in Britain with nine genera, *Lysimachia* having four species. The commonest is the one here described, another familiar one being the Creeping Jenny, *L. nummularia* L., which creeps on the ground, rooting at the nodes. The other two species, *L. thyrsiflora* L., with axillary spike-like racemes, and *L. nemorum* L., resembling the Creeping Jenny, but with long slender flower-stalks, are much less common.

---

120. Scarlet Pimpernel, Poor-Man's Weather-glass, *Anagallis arvensis* L. ($\times \frac{2}{5}$); a small often much-branched procumbent annual, with branches from an inch or two up to a foot long, acutely angled or narrowly winged; leaves opposite, sessile, ovate, rounded at the base, triangular at the apex, 3-nerved from the base, minutely roughened on the margin; flowers (A, $\times 1\frac{3}{5}$), usually red, axillary, solitary, with stalks longer than the leaves, the stalks recurving in fruit; calyx (B, $\times 2\frac{2}{5}$) deeply 5-lobed

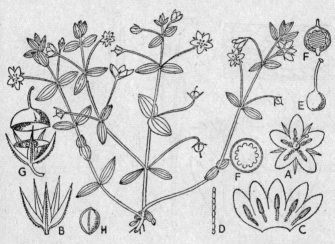

nearly to the base, lobes lanceolate, very acute, with a keel-like midrib and thin whitish margins; corolla (C, $\times 2\frac{2}{5}$) with a very short tube, 5-lobed, lobes rounded and very minutely fringed with glands; stamens 5, opposite the corolla-lobes and inserted on the tube; stalks (filaments) fringed with several-celled hairs (D, $\times 10$); ovary (E, $\times 2\frac{1}{2}$) globose, 1-locular with several ovules arranged on a free central placenta which does not reach the top or the loculus (F, $\times 3\frac{1}{2}$); fruit (G, $\times 1\frac{3}{5}$) a dry capsule splitting transversely around the middle, the upper part with the persistent style resembling a Chinaman's cap; seeds (H, $\times 6$) several, triangular, and with narrowly winged margins (family *Primulaceae*).

121. Primrose, *Primula vulgaris* Huds. (flower and leaf × $\frac{4}{5}$); perennial with a rosette of bright green leaves, these oblong-oblanceolate, with wavy and finely toothed margins, and wrinkled (bullate) reticulate upper surface, very coarsely reticulate below and with softly hairy nerves and veins (A, × $1\frac{1}{4}$); flowers sweet-scented, the stalks arising from the root, often as long as or longer than the leaves, softly hairy; calyx tubular, 5-ribbed and narrowly 5-lobed, softly hairy outside; corolla cream yellow, tubular, the tube a little longer than the calyx, 5-lobed, the lobes (B, × $\frac{4}{5}$) twisted (contorted) in bud, deeply notched and with wavy margins,

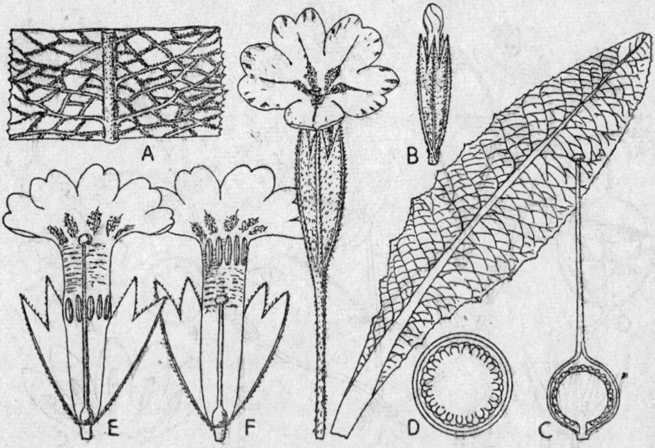

suffused at the base with orange; stamens inserted either about the middle of the corolla-tube or within its throat, opposite the corolla-lobes; anthers facing inwards; ovary (C, × $\frac{3}{5}$) rounded, with a slender style either reaching only to the middle of the corolla or to its mouth; ovules numerous, arranged around the central axis (D, × 2) of the 1-locular ovary; fruit a capsule opening at the top by 5 teeth (family *Primulaceae*).

The flowers are of great biological interest and vertical sections of the two forms are shown. Figure E (× $1\frac{1}{4}$) shows the long-styled or pin-eyed form, with the stigma filling the throat of the corolla and the anthers attached in the middle of the tube. Figure F (× $1\frac{1}{4}$) shows the short-styled or thrum-eyed form, with the position of these organs reversed.

122. Cowslip, *Primula veris* L. (× ⅖); perennial with a dense tuft of numerous slender roots; leaves all basal (radical) mostly ascending, oblong-oblanceolate to oblong-elliptic and often very abruptly narrowed into and decurrent on the stalks, finely toothed, very minutely pubescent; common flower stalks several from amongst the leaves and overtopping them considerably, very shortly and softly hairy, bearing at the top an umbel of several stalked, scented flowers, with a whorl of narrow bracts at the base of the stalks; calyx about

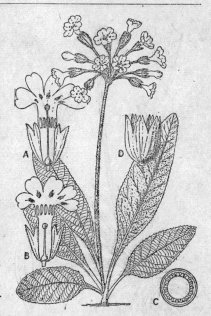

½ in. long, shortly 5-lobed, softly hairy; corolla cream-yellow usually with an orange patch at the base of each lobe, the tube expanded about the middle in the long-styled form (A, × 1½) and towards the top in the short-styled form (B, × 1½); lobes 5, notched; stamens 5, inserted either in the middle or towards the top of the tube; ovary superior, 1-locular (C, × 6), with a style reaching to the middle of the corolla-tube or nearly to the top (short- and long-styled forms respectively); fruit (D, × ⅔) a bell-shaped 5-lobed capsule about ⅔ in. long, enclosed by the persistent calyx (family *Primulaceae*).

The notes about the two forms of flowers in the Primrose (fig. 121) apply equally well to those of the Cowslip, and hybrids between them occur which have been and are easily mistaken for another species, the real Oxslip, *P. elatior* Schreb., which, however is much more rare and is found only in East Anglia. Nectar is secreted around the base of the ovary, and the corolla-tube is sometimes perforated by humble-bees.

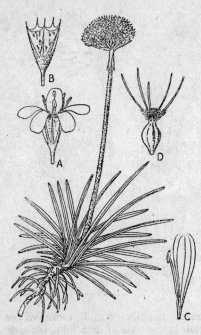

123. Sea Thrift, *Armeria maritima* Willd. ($\times \frac{2}{5}$); a tufted perennial, rootstock branched, covered by the remains of the old leaf-bases; leaves numerous, grass-like and forming a dense rosette, narrowly linear, entire, obtuse at the apex, minutely hairy; flowering stems single from each rosette, leafless, covered with short soft hairs, up to about 9 in. high, bearing at the top a globose head of usually pink or sometimes white flowers (A, $\times 1\frac{1}{4}$); outer bracts longer than the others and elongated at the base and forming a reflexed sheath around the top of the peduncle; inner bracts broader and becoming membranous, those below the flowers very thin and transparent; calyx (B, $\times$ 2) tubular, of 5 lobes, lobes very narrow but united into a membranous tube with the short sharp calyx teeth at the top, lower part green and pubescent; petals (C, $\times$ 2) narrowly obovate, with narrow claws, free to the base; stamens 5, opposite to and inserted at the base of the petals; filaments slender, pale, anthers facing inwards, lemon yellow; ovary (D, $\times$ 6) laterally 5-lobed, but with only one loculus and a single pendulous ovule; styles 5, free, with spreading rod-like hairs at the base (family *Plumbaginaceae*).

Very common around our coasts in muddy and sandy places and on maritime rocks; also high up in some of the Cumberland and Scottish mountains. The most striking feature is the basal prolongation of the outer bracts of the involucre to form a jagged tubular sheath around the top of the peduncle.

PLANTAIN, *Plantago lanceolata* L., *Plantago major* L., and *Plantago media* L.

124. Plantain, *Plantago lanceolata* L., *Plantago major* L., and *Plantago media* L. (habit drawings much reduced, floral parts × 2). There are three common species of Plantain in Britain, and sketches of these are shown in the drawing, the other two being confined to maritime districts (*P. maritima* L. and *P. coronopus* L.). Of these three the most common is *P. lanceolata* (A), with erect or spreading lanceolate leaves minutely and distantly toothed on the margin with 3–6 longitudinal nerves and gradually narrowed into 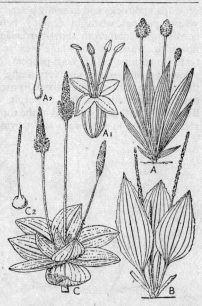 the petiole; the spikes are ovoid or oblong and not usually more than an inch long, and the fruit contains 2 seeds. In *P. major* (B) the leaves are ascending and very broadly ovate and stalked and lined with 5 or more nerves according to width; the spike is narrow and slender and sometimes elongates up to about 15 inches; the fruit contains several seeds. In *P. media* (C) the leaves form a flat rosette on the ground, are very broad and sessile or with a wide very short stalk and usually 5 longitudinal nerves converging on the apex; the spike is intermediate between the other two species described here, at most about 2 in. long but narrower than in *P. lanceolata*. *P. media* is found mainly in limestone districts, but the other two are very abundant in almost any kind of soil. *P. lanceolata*, especially, is a very common pasture plant (family *Plantaginaceae*).

The flowers of Plantains are wind-pollinated, the stamens having long slender flexible filaments, and the styles feathery stigmas. Insects visit the flowers for the sake of their pollen.

125. Golden Stonecrop, *Sedum acre* L. ($\times \frac{2}{5}$); grows in tufts on walls and rocks and in sandy places, forming bright green and yellow patches when in flower; perennial and procumbent, consisting of numerous short barren leafy stems and erect leafy flowering branches, the whole very succulent and bitter to the taste (sometimes called Wall-pepper); leaves alternate or rarely a few opposite, sessile and very fleshy, ovoid or nearly globose, those on the barren shoots especially arranged in several rows and densely crowded, on the flowering shoots more scattered; flowers (A, nat. size) crowded at the top of the shoots, eventually spreading out in fruit into short cymes; sepals 5, short and

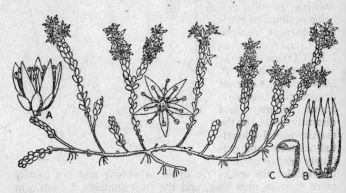

fleshy like the leaves; petals free, bright yellow, ovate-lanceolate, acute; stamens 10, in 2 rows, the outer row opposite the sepals, the inner row opposite the petals; carpels (B, $\times$ 4) 5, free from one another, each with a nectariferous notched scale outside between their bases and the stamens; fruits splitting along the inner side, and containing numerous very small seeds attached to the inner angle (C, $\times$ 6) (family *Crassulaceae*).

The five outer stamens are the first to mature and when they have shed their pollen bend back towards the sepals; then the other five anthers open, after which the very small terminal stigmas of the five carpels mature and are cross-pollinated by insects.

The succulent leaves are very characteristic of this family, to which also the Penny-wort (fig. 126) belongs. Numerous species occur in dry rocky regions, especially in the Karoo of southern Africa, and in rocky districts of Europe and Central Asia.

126. Navel-Wort, Penny-Wort, *Umbilicus pendulinus* DC. ($\times \frac{2}{5}$); perennial and almost woody at the base, the basal part of the stem curved; basal leaves on long stalks which gradually decrease in length upwards, the blade fleshy, orbicular, attached in the middle, crenate on the margin, the upper leaves gradually merging into bracts, the stalk becoming basal; flowers (A, $\times$ 2) usually solitary in the axils of the bracts, pendulous except when quite young; calyx divided into 5 narrow lobes; corolla (B, $\times$ 2) tubular, about $\frac{1}{3}$ in. long, with 5 short ovate-triangular acute lobes;

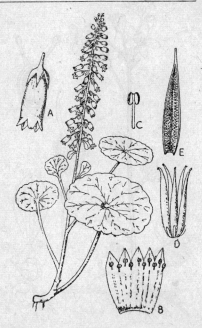

stamens 10, adnate to the top of the corolla-tube, in 2 rows, the upper row opposite the corolla-lobes, the lower alternate with them; anther-lobes separate (C, $\times$ 8); carpels (D, $\times$ 3) 5, free from one another, each with a scale at the base, and gradually narrowed into the style; fruiting carpels (E, $\times$ 5) splitting up the inner side and releasing the very numerous minute brown seeds (family *Crassulaceae*). (Recorded in most botanical works as *Cotyledon umbilicus* L. or *C. umbilicus-veneris* L.)

This grows often in great abundance in some districts, particularly near the coast from the south-west of England to south-west of Scotland, mostly on rocks, walls and old buildings; in damp and shady hedge bottoms, sometimes 2–3 ft. high. It is an interesting plant from the evolutionary point of view, showing the rare combination of free carpels (a primitive feature) and the petals united into a tube (a comparatively advanced feature).

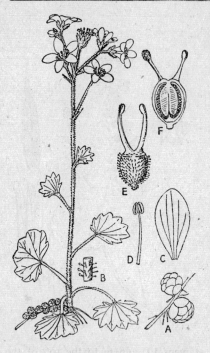

127. Meadow Saxifrage, *Saxifraga granulata* L. ($\times \frac{2}{5}$); perennial with small globose bulb-like structures (A, $\times 1\frac{1}{4}$) covered with whitish or brown scales; stems erect, up to about 1 ft. high, hairy, the hairs in the lower part long and without gland-tips, those higher up shorter and tipped by a gland (B, $\times 1\frac{1}{2}$); lower leaves kidney shaped, coarsely toothed and sometimes almost lobed, very few on the stem and these becoming sessile, stalks and margins fringed with longish white hairs; flowers few in small terminal cymes (see below); bracts linear, like the deeply 5-lobed calyx (which is above the ovary) covered with gland-tipped hairs; tips of calyx lobes sometimes tinged with dull crimson; petals (C, $\times 1\frac{1}{2}$) 5, free, white, lined with green in the lower half, about $\frac{1}{2}$ in. long; stamens (D, $\times 1\frac{1}{2}$) 10 (see below); ovary (E, $\times 2$) partly below the calyx (semi-inferior), 1-locular, with a large thick placenta hanging from the apex, split in two at the bottom and bearing very numerous ovules (F, $\times 2\frac{1}{2}$); seeds numerous in the capsule (family *Saxifragaceae*).

The stamens mature before the stigmas, and the central flower of the cluster opens first and differs markedly from the others in having the large fat papillous stigmas borne on long styles which become very conspicuous after the stamens have shed their pollen. Sometimes this central flower has the alternate stamens less polleniferous or almost sterile, whilst all the stamens of the lateral flowers are equally fertile.

128. Golden Saxifrage, *Chrysosplenium oppositifolium* L. (× ⅔); a delicate perennial herb in wet shady places and rill-sides, growing up to an altitude of more than 3,000 ft. in the Scottish and Welsh mountains; usually found in considerable patches; stems a few inches high, rooting at the lower nodes; leaves opposite, stalked, orbicular to obovate, undulate-crenate on the margin, without visible nerves and no stipules, sometimes with a few stiffish hairs on the upper surface and minutely speckled with brown, those around the flowers often streaked with golden yellow like the flowers; stem divided into two at the top and forming 2 small cymes of a few golden-yellow or greenish flowers (A, × 3), each flower subtended by a small leaf; middle flower sessile or nearly so, lateral flowers shortly stalked; calyx-tube joined to the lower half of the ovary, 4-lobed, lobes ovate; stamens (B, × 8) 8, 4 alternate with and 4 opposite the sepals; anthers very small and rounded; between the stamens and ovary a broad crenate spreading disk; ovary half-inferior, consisting of two united spreading pointed divergent carpels, 1-locular, with numerous ovules attached to the walls; fruit (C, × 6) a capsule splitting along the top, with numerous small reddish brown seeds (D, × 8) (family *Saxifragaceae*).

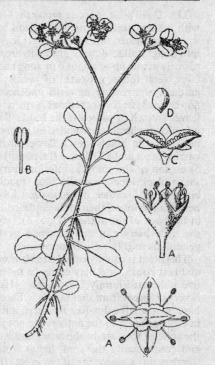

The large, prominent disk surrounding the base of the upper half of the ovary secretes nectar, which forms in drops and spreads out in a thin layer, and attracts numerous short-tongued insects.

129. Devil's-Bit, *Succisa pratensis* Moench. ($\times \frac{1}{2}$); perennial with a short thick rootstock; stems and leaves thinly clothed with long rather stiff hairs; basal leaves oblanceolate, tapered into long stalks, entire, gradually narrowed to the apex but scarcely acute, up to about 8 in. long and $1\frac{1}{2}$ in. wide, thin, with a faint very loose network of veins; stem leaves opposite, gradually narrowing upwards and becoming linear, the lateral flower-head stalks sometimes with a pair of small bract-like leaves an inch or so below the head; flowers (B, $\times 2\frac{1}{2}$) collected into globose heads surrounded by an involucre of about 2 rows of narrow green bracts; each flower in the head subtended by a narrow bract and a little cup (involucel) with 5 teeth; calyx (E, $\times$ 5) on top of the smooth, inferior ovary, deeply 4–5-lobed with sharp black lobes; corolla blue, tubular, the tube hairy, with either 4 or 5 rather unequal-sized lobes; stamens 4, inserted between the lobes, their stalks inflexed in bud, filament attached at the back of the anthers (D, $\times 5$); style slender; fruit girt by the little hairy cup and crowned by the calyx, with a single pendulous seed (family *Dipsacaceae*).

This plant is usually called *Scabiosa succisa* L. in British Floras and text books, and may easily be mistaken by the beginner for one of the daisy family, *Compositae*. Its floral structure, however is very different from that family. Each flower is enclosed at the base by a small calyx-like *involucel*, a like structure never found in *Compositae*, and the anthers are not joined into a tube around the style as they are in the latter family. In addition the ovule, and consequently the seed, hangs from the top of the ovary, whereas in *Compositae* it is erect from the base. *Succisa pratensis* differs from the other less common members of its genus in having entire leaves and the outer flowers of the head not markedly larger than the others. Nectar is secreted in the smooth narrow base of the corolla-tube, which is lined just above by stiff hairs. The stamens are curved downwards in bud (A, $\times 3$), and when the flower opens straighten up in succession, and their anthers release the pollen and fall off (B and C). After this the style lengthens, and the stigma becomes receptive and cross-pollination is effected by insects.

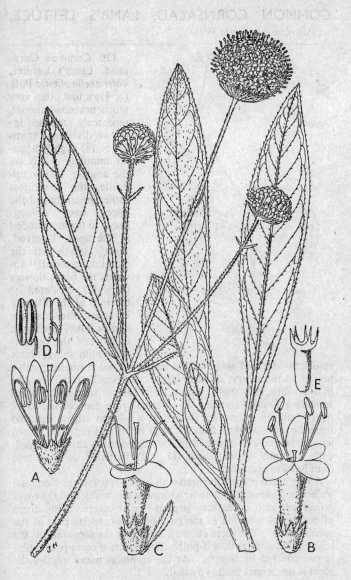

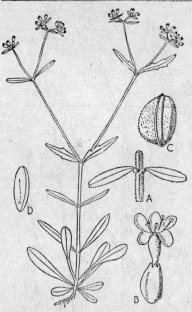

130. Common Corn-salad, Lamb's Lettuce, *Valerianella olitoria* Poll. ($\times \frac{2}{5}$); a low often very much branched annual, repeatedly branched into two divisions; stems (A, $\times 1\frac{1}{2}$) slightly angular, minutely bristly on the angles; leaves opposite, the lowermost rather spoon-shaped, the upper ones oblong-linear to linear, rounded at the apex, 1-nerved, shortly bristly on the margins, especially towards the base; flowers (B, $\times 12$) clustered at the ends of the ultimate branches, often a sessile middle flower already in fruit when the remainder are blooming; bracts similar in size and shape to the leaves but much smaller; calyx united to the ovary, divided into 5 very small teeth; corolla bluish white, very small, with a short slender tube and 5 equal spreading lobes; stamens 3, exserted from the corolla-tube; ovary inferior, grooved; style with a 3-lobed stigma exserted from the corolla-tube; fruit (C, $\times 5$) small and nut-like, ribbed lengthwise and with a groove on one side, minutely hairy, 1-seeded, with 2 empty loculi; seed (D, $\times 5$) flattened on one side (family *Valerianaceae*).

A very small plant compared with its tall relative, the Common Valerian, *Valeriana officinalis*, which is a perennial, and the calyx grows out into a feathery pappus-like structure. Tiny drops of nectar are secreted at the base of the expanded part of the corolla-tube. The three stamens mature at the same time as the stigmas and automatic self-pollination occurs if cross-pollination is not effected by insects. As the common name implies the plant is sometimes used as a salad.

131. Marsh Penny-wort, *Hydrocotyle vulgaris* L. ($\times \frac{2}{5}$);
perennial with slender stems creeping along wet mud or floating
in water, rooting and giving off a leaf or leaves and flower stalks
at every node; leaves (A, $\times \frac{4}{5}$) orbicular, attached in the middle
to the long stalk, crenate and often very shortly lobed, with as
many nerves as lobes radiating from the point of junction with
the stalk; peduncles shorter than the leaf-stalks, with a single or
more clusters of flowers towards the top; flowers (B, $\times$ 2)
minute, with a scarcely evident calyx and tiny free petals on top

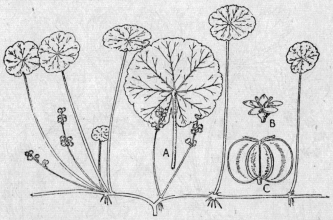

of the ovary; stamens as many as petals; ovary inferior, with
2 spreading styles, soon expanding into a rounded though very
small compressed fruit (C, $\times$ 5) widely notched at each end;
flowers in summer and easily recognised amongst the family
Umbelliferae by the orbicular leaves attached in the middle
(peltate).

This is a striking little plant which the beginner at first sight
may think has not much relationship with the hemlock family to
which it belongs. The clusters of very small flowers form very
imperfect umbels. Only one other fairly common British plant
has very similar leaves, this being the ordinary Penny-wort,
Umbilicus pendulinus, shown in fig. 126.

132. Wood Sanicle, *Sanicula europaea* L. ($\times \frac{2}{3}$); rootstock short and rather woody; leaves nearly all radical, with purplish based expanded stalks much longer than the blade, the latter rounded or pentagonal in outline and divided almost to the base into 5 obovate lobes, these again lobed and toothed, the teeth incurved to the margin and with very sharp points, the principal nerves even more prominent above than below; flowering stems up to about $1\frac{1}{2}$ ft. high, leafless or bearing one or two smaller ones which gradually become reduced to bracts below the inflorescence

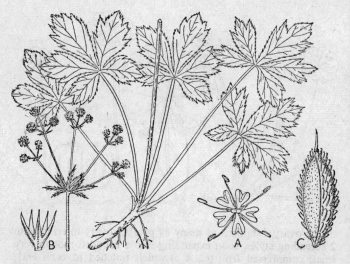

and these sessile; flower-heads (really very small umbels) few in terminal panicles; all the umbels with an involucre of small bracts; flowers (A, $\times$ 8) unisexual, the males in 2 or 3 rows around the females; calyx (B, $\times$ 8) deeply 5-lobed; petals white, tinged with pink, obovate, with markedly inflexed tips; stamens much longer than the petals; fruit (C, $\times$ 6) about $\frac{1}{8}$ in. long, narrowly ellipsoid, covered with hooked prickles (family *Umbelliferae*).

On account of the flowers being nearly sessile in small globose head-like clusters, the beginner will probably not at first recognise this as belonging to the Hemlock family, but may mistake it for the Rose family (*Rosaceae*), as the leaves resemble those of some members of that group.

133. Wild Carrot, *Daucus carota* L. ($\times \frac{2}{5}$); an erect annual or biennial with a branched stem up to 3 ft. high, with a carrot-like tap root; stems closely ribbed and clothed, especially towards the base and at the nodes, with stiff bristle-like hairs; lower leaves bipinnate, long-stalked, the ultimate segments deeply cut into acute lanceolate lobes; basal sheath with a narrow membranous margin bristly at the base; upper leaves becoming much smaller and less cut up; umbels terminal and opposite to the leaves, on rather stout common stalks with bristly bulbous-based hairs; 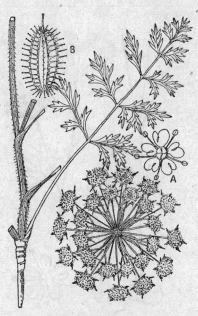 general umbel girt by narrow 3-forked bracts with broad membranous sheathing bases conspicuous in the bud stage; ultimate umbels numerous, surrounded by several narrow bracts with membranous margins and fringed with hairs; flowers (A, $\times$ 3) with minute calyx; petals white, broadly obovate, notched into 2 unequal lobes with sharply inflexed tips; stamens a little longer than the petals; ovary covered with short bristly hairs; ribs of the carpels (B, $\times$ 4) covered with sharp bristles like the teeth of a comb, the bristles with very minute reflexed tips (family *Umbelliferae*).

This is the wild form of the cultivated Carrot of our gardens, its original habitat being the sea-coasts of southern Europe, but now found in fields and waste places; it flowers during the summer and autumn. Near the sea the leaves are more fleshy, this form being distinguished as *D. maritimus*.

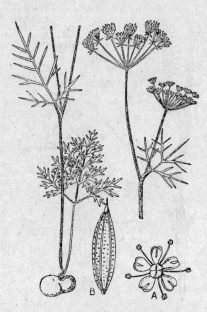

134. Pignut, Earth Nut, *Conopodium majus* (Gouan) Lor. & Barr. ($\times \frac{2}{5}$); perennial with a rounded or 2-lobed tuberous rootstock; stems annual, erect, slender, up to about 2 ft. high, simple or slightly branched, glabrous and closely ribbed; basal leaves few, soon disappearing, divided into 3 stalked segments, these deeply bipinnate into fine sharp narrow lobes; stem leaves sessile on the broad basal sheath, deeply and bipinnately divided into fine linear acute segments, the end lobe usually appreciably longer and a little broader than the others, all with minutely rough margins; main umbel which flowers first opposite the last leaf, with a younger lateral umbel, and usually one or two umbels terminating lateral axillary branches below; common stalks very slender, especially of the lateral umbels; main umbel without an involucre, only the ultimate small umbels with a few narrow bracts; rays of flowers about $\frac{1}{2}$ in. diam., the stalks thread-like; flowers (A, $\times$ 4) very small, white; calyx minute; petals obovate, with inflexed points; stamens longer than the petals; fruits (B, $\times$ 3) narrowly elliptic, about $\frac{1}{3}$ in. long, each carpel with 5 faint ribs and very slender vittas between (family *Umbelliferae*).

This plant flowers in summer and grows in woods and fields.

135. Fool's Parsley, **Aethusa cynapium** L. (× ½); an erect annual up to 2 ft. high, but sometimes very dwarf; stems ribbed, with a nauseous odour when rubbed; leaves glaucous-green, with long ribbed basal sheaths ½–1 in. long and with a broad membranous margin produced beyond the tip; blade 2–3 times pinnate, with lanceolate acute lobes, glabrous; umbels on rather short common stalks opposite to the leaves; main umbel without an involucre of bracts; ultimate small umbels with about 3 linear

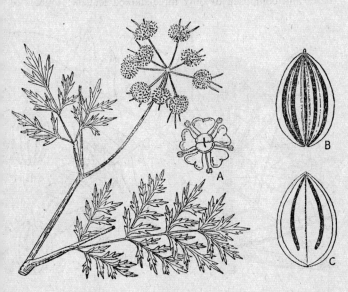

bracts all on the outer side of the cluster; rays about 9, up to ½ in. diam., flowers (A, × 3) with minute calyx; petals white, broadly obovate, notched at the apex; fruit ovate, compressed, the carpels (B, × 3) with 5 very thick prominent ribs and 5 narrow black vittas between the ribs, on the inside of the carpel (C, × 3) only two vittas not extending to the base (family *Umbelliferae*).

This plant may be at once recognised amongst our native *Umbelliferae* by the bracts below the ultimate small clusters of flowers, these being few and arranged only on the *outer side* of the clusters. It is a common weed and regarded as poisonous.

136. Cow Parsnip, Hogweed, *Heracleum sphondylium* L. ($\times\frac{1}{2}$); a coarse plant up to about 6 ft. high, stem hollow, angular and furrowed, hispid with stiff bristle-like hairs; leaves large, pinnate, with up to 9 leaflets, the latter broad and irregularly lobed and toothed, the lowermost stalked, the upper sessile and more or less decurrent on the common stalk, more markedly bristly at the joints, as well as shorter hairs all over the lower surface; stem leaves gradually becoming sessile on very large hispid sheathing bases and composed of only three stalked leaflets; umbels of

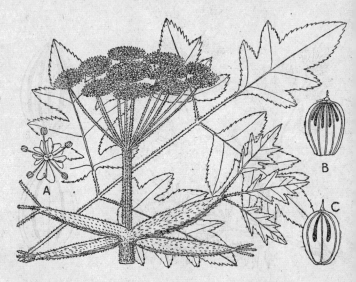

several to many rays, the primary umbel usually without bracts; ultimate umbels with an involucre of very narrow bracts; flowers (A, $\times$ 2) with a minute calyx; petals white, unequal-sized, wedge-shaped, widely notched and with inflexed points; stamens longer than the petals; ovary covered with woolly hairs; carpels (B, $\times$ 1$\frac{1}{2}$) with 5 slender ribs and a single vitta between each, these do not extend to the base; on the reverse side of the carpel (C, $\times$ 1$\frac{1}{2}$) only two vittas visible extending about half way down (family *Umbelliferae*).

This striking plant grows in hedges, open places in woods, and in moist meadows. It flowers in summer and autumn.

137. Wild Angelica, *Angelica sylvestris* L. ($\times \frac{2}{5}$); perennial with a stout stem up to 4 or 5 ft. high, minutely hairy in the upper part; lower leaves large, twice pinnate, with rather large leaflets in threes, the terminal leaflet ovate to obovate and mostly equal-sided at the narrowed base, the lateral leaflets more or less elliptic and unequal-sided at the base, all acutely triangular at the apex and coarsely toothed like a saw (serrate), paler and shortly hairy below especially on the nerves, the stem leaves gradually smaller upwards and reduced to the large sheathing base and a few small segments; umbels usually 3 together at the

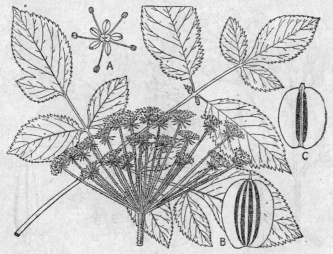

tops of the shoots, the middle flowering first and rather shorter than the two lateral, the primary umbels usually without bracts or of 2–3 linear bracts, the ultimate umbels with several narrow short bracts scarcely wider than the pedicels; rays 25–40, their stalks shortly hairy; flowers' (A, $\times$ 2) with minute calyx; petals white, elliptic, with inflexed apex; stamens with long thread-like filaments; carpels (B, $\times$ 2) flattened, about $\frac{1}{8}$ in. long, with 3 ribs on the back and 4 vittas between, broadly winged, on the reverse side (C, $\times$ 2) with only 2 vittas showing parallel against the middle (family *Umbelliferae*).

This species is easily distinguished in fruit by the double wing, the wing of each carpel becoming free before they separate.

138. Wild Parsley, Keck, *Anthriscus sylvestris* Hoffm. ($\times \frac{2}{5}$); perennial with a tap root; stems up to 3 or 4 ft. high, hollow, very shortly hairy, but becoming glabrous higher up except at the nodes which have a fringe of longer hairs; lower leaves with a long stalk between the sheathing base and the twice pinnate blade, the ultimate lobes deeply and pinnately lobulate with acute teeth; upper leaves gradually smaller and sessile on the broad fringed sheath, all slightly hairy especially on the nerves below; primary umbel (A, $\times \frac{2}{5}$) arising from the fork with a pair of small leaves, but without a general involucre; ultimate small umbels with about

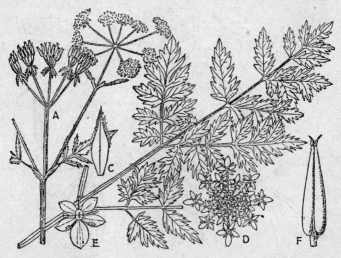

5 or 6 bracts (B, $\times \frac{2}{5}$) resembling a calyx, these (C, $\times 2$) fringed with hairs and reflexed in flower; rays of the first umbel (in the fork) usually 3–5, of the terminal umbels about 8 or 9; flowers white (D, nat. size), about 15 in each partial umbel, the outer flowers (E, $\times 2$) with the outer petals larger than the others; styles very short in the middle of a pale flat fleshy disk; fruits (F, $\times 2$) about $\frac{1}{3}$ in. long, narrow, smooth and shining, with 2 antennae-like styles at the top, but neither ribbed nor with resin canals (family *Umbelliferae*).

This is one of the most common of the hemlock family in Britain, and it grows in hedges, on the borders of fields, etc., being the first of the family to flower.

GOUTWEED, BISHOP'S WEED, HERB GERARD,

Aegopodium podagraria L.

139. Goutweed, Bishop's Weed, Herb Gerard, *Aegopodium podagraria* L. ($\times \frac{2}{5}$); an aggressive perennial with a creeping root-stock; radical leaves on long stalks and often forming a complete carpet on the ground, twice ternate; lateral leaflets very unequal-sided at the base, oblong or oblong-elliptic, acutely pointed, terminal leaflet ovate or ovate-elliptic, those of the lateral divisions unequal-sided at the base, but of the terminal division mostly equal-sided, all rather coarsely toothed (crenate); stem

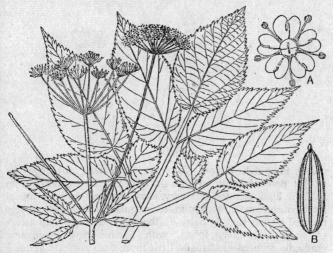

leaves becoming sessile on the broad glabrous basal sheath with membranous margins and reduced to three leaflets; umbels usually 3 together terminating the main shoot, the middle one opening first and often overtopped by the others; general and ultimate umbels without an involucre of bracts; rays numerous; flowers (A, $\times$ 6) very small, white, on rather short stalks; calyx minute; petals rounded-obovate, deeply notched and with an inflexed point; stamens a little longer than the petals; carpels (B, $\times$ 4) with 5 slender ribs, but no resinous vittas (family *Umbelliferae*).

This is a notorious weed which is difficult to eradicate when once it has become established. It is supposed to have been introduced and cultivated in the Middle Ages, and is usually most plentiful near buildings. It flowers from June to August.

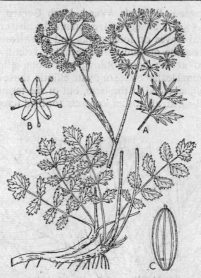

140. Pimpinel, Burnet Saxifrage, *Pimpinella saxifraga* L.
($\times \frac{2}{5}$); perennial with a rather thick rootstock; stems erect, up
to 2 ft. high, slender and wiry, very minutely hairy; radical
leaves once pinnate, with rounded irregularly lobed and coarsely
toothed leaflets slightly hairy on the nerves below; stem leaves
(A, $\times \frac{2}{5}$) bipinnately lobed, with narrow acute segments,
gradually reduced upwards to little more than a sheath about $\frac{3}{4}$
in. long with paler margins and a sharp tip and streaked with
nerves; umbels usually 2 together, the primary (first to flower)
usually a little shorter than the other, all without bracts; rays
10–18, very slender; flowers (B, $\times$ 4) 15–20 in each cluster;
petals white, narrowly elliptic, with an inflexed tip; stems longer
than the petals; fruit (C, $\times$ 5) ovoid, scarcely compressed, the
carpels with 5 slightly prominent ribs (family *Umbelliferae*).

Flowers all summer and is found in pastures, on banks and by
roadsides. The well-known Aniseed is the fruit of a related
species, *Pimpinella anisum* L., a native of the Eastern Mediterranean and cultivated in many countries, especially in Spain,
South Russia and Bulgaria. It is most familiar as an ingredient
of " seed " cakes.

180

141. Harebell, Scotch Bluebell, *Campanula rotundifolia* L. ($\times \frac{2}{5}$); a perennial with a slender creeping rootstock; basal stems erect or ascending, but rather weak, up to 1½ ft. or rarely 2 ft. high; leaves rounded, heart-shaped at the base, often withering and disappearing by flowering time, undulately toothed on the margin; stem-leaves alternate, narrowly lanceolate to linear, only the lowermost a little broader, entire or rarely with a few obscure teeth, glabrous; flowers blue, few, nodding, in a loose terminal raceme or panicle or sometimes solitary; calyx-lobes 5, on top of

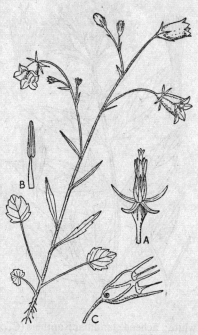

the ovary, linear, not as long as the corolla-tube, the latter bell-shaped and about ½ in. long, with 5 broad short lobes; stamens (B, × 2) 5, inserted within the base of the corolla; anthers included in the tube, free from each other; ovary inferior; style nearly as long as the corolla, divided into 3 short stigmas; capsule (C, × ½) ovoid or globose, pendulous, opening by pores near the base (A, flower with corolla removed, × 1½) (family *Campanulaceae*).

The Harebell, or the Bluebell of Scotland and northern England, is very widely distributed in north temperate regions, right from the Mediterranean to the Arctic Circle, sometimes at great elevations, and it is common in the northern United States of America and in Canada. Young botanists are often puzzled by the specific name, as the rounded basal leaves to which it applies have often quite disappeared at flowering time.

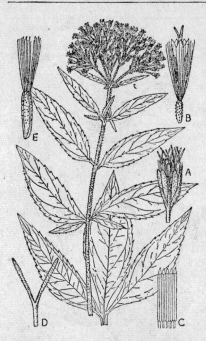

142. Hemp Agrimony, *Eupatorium cannabinum* L. ($\times \frac{2}{5}$); perennial in damp places by river and road sides and on moors, flowering late summer and autumn; stems with purplish jointed hairs; stem-leaves opposite, gland-dotted below, mostly divided into 3 lanceolate acuminate toothed leaflets, those of the smaller branches often undivided; flower-heads (A, $\times$ 2) crowded into compound clusters, pink, reddish, or nearly white; flower-head bracts few and loose; flowers (B, $\times$ 3) about 5 in each head, tubular and bisexual; corolla 5-lobed; pappus-hairs white; achene glandular; anthers (C, $\times$ 6) with barren tips and rounded bases; style (D, $\times$ 4) with 2 spreading branches shortly hairy in the upper part, stigmatic in the lowermost fourth; ripe achenes ("seeds") (E, $\times$ 6) ribbed (family *Compositae*).

The common name of this plant is due to the leaves resembling those of hemp. It usually grows in clumps on banks near water, and is widely distributed in Europe and Asia. The heads are much reduced in size, and are individually not very conspicuous, but this is compensated for by their aggregation into a dense corymb. These are conspicuous because the margins of the involucral bracts are reddish, and the protruding stylar branches are white. The latter are very hairy all around, and these hairs serve to sweep out the pollen from the anther-cylinder, retaining them so that insects visiting the flowers brush against them and carry them to another flower.

143. Goldenrod, *Solidago virga-aurea* L. (× ⅖); perennial herb with annual slightly woody stems up to 2½ ft. high, prominently ribbed and softly hairy; radical leaves narrowly obovate, coarsely toothed (serrate), stalked, soon withering; stem leaves oblanceolate, acute at the apex, long-tapered to the base, gradually smaller upwards, minutely hairy on the margins and very obscurely and distantly toothed; flower-heads in a narrow oblong leafy panicle, the leaves gradually reduced upwards to small bracts; stalks very short; involucral bracts in about 5 rows, gradually increasing in size upwards, with a green midrib very shortly hairy; flowers bright yellow, the rays (A, × 3), 10–12, the limb toothed at the tip; disk flowers (B, × 2¼) about twice as many; anthers rounded at the base (C, × 3); achenes hairy, with a white finely toothed pappus (E, × 5) nearly as long as the corolla-tube (D, style-arms, × 4) (family *Compositae*).

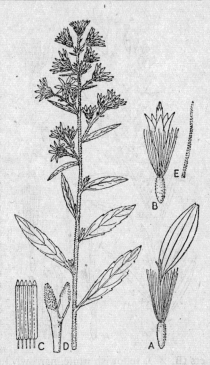

The chief interest in this species is that it is the only European and Asiatic representative of a large North American genus. It is very like many species of *Aster* in the latter region, but with yellow ray flowers, which are produced in summer and autumn, like so many others of the *Aster* tribe to which it belongs.

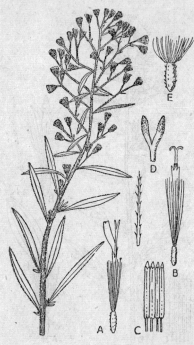

144. Canadian Erigeron, *Erigeron canadensis* L. ($\times \frac{2}{5}$); annual 1–2 ft. high; stems slender, thinly clothed with rather stiff hairs, prominently ribbed; seedling leaves spoon-shaped or obovate, entire or slightly toothed; stem leaves linear-oblanceolate, acute, slightly toothed or entire, fringed with rather stiff hairs; flower-heads numerous, in a terminal leafy panicle, with slender stalks; involucral bracts in about 2 rows, slender, green, with pale thin margins; ray-flowers (A, × 3) small and inconspicuous, white or tinged with purple, with a slender and very small blade; disk flowers (B, × 3) yellowish white, narrowly tubular; anthers (C, × 3) rounded at the base, produced at the apex; style-branches (D, × 4) hairy all over in the upper part; achenes (E, × 3) ("seeds") cylindric, not ribbed, slightly hairy, topped with a spreading white pappus of minutely toothed (barbellate) bristles (family *Compositae*).

A native of North America, and now widely spread nearly all over the world as a weed in cultivated and waste places and by roadsides. It flowers during summer and autumn.

145. Daisy, *Bellis perennis* L. ($\times \frac{2}{5}$); very dwarf perennial, with a short rootstock; leaves all from the base (radical), spoon-shaped to obovate, more or less toothed and pubescent; flower-head stalks (peduncles) one or more from each tuft of leaves, bearing a single head, variable in size but usually about $\frac{3}{4}$ in. diam.; bracts of the involucre (B, $\times 1\frac{3}{4}$) very dark green, more or less in two rows, narrowly oblong, with long scattered several-celled hairs outside;

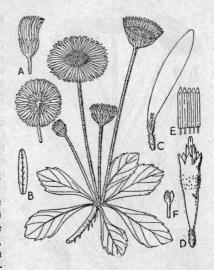

receptacle ovoid, hollow; ray-flowers (C, $\times 3$) numerous in 2–3 rows, white or the tips tinged with pink outside; corolla-tube clothed with a few long hairs; blade (limb) entire or slightly toothed at the apex; disk flowers (D, $\times 6$) numerous, rich cream-yellow; corolla-tube slightly hairy above the middle; anthers (E, $\times 6$) with narrowly triangular tops, rounded at the base; style-branches (F, $\times 6$) very short and broad, hairy on the outside; achenes slightly hairy, without a pappus (family *Compositae*).

This neat and much beloved little plant is, of course, known to almost everyone from early childhood. It is only found in Europe as far east as the Caucasus, though the genus, a small one, is distributed over the temperate regions of the whole of the northern hemisphere. In Britain it flowers nearly all the year round and is among the first to bloom in very early spring. Though the Daisy is capable of spreading rapidly, as owners of lawns know to their cost, it possesses no pappus to assist its distribution by the wind like so many other members of the family *Compositae*. A notable feature is the closing of the heads at night and during dull weather (A, $\times \frac{2}{5}$).

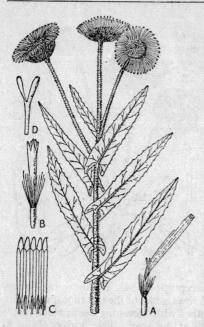

146. Greater Flea-bane, *Pulicaria dysenterica* (L.) Gaertn. ($\times \frac{2}{3}$); greyish green perennial with creeping rootstock, by the banks of ditches, damp places by roadsides and in damp pastures; stems erect, densely leafy, ribbed, white woolly-hairy like the under-surface of the leaves; leaves sessile, oblong-lanceolate, arrow-shaped at the base, rather thin and toothed (dentate); flower-heads usually 3 or more at the end of each stem or branch, about 1–1½ in. diam.; involucral bracts numerous, very narrow with thread-like tips; ray-flowers (A, $\times$ 2) numerous, yellow, spreading, very narrow, with 3 teeth at the top; pappus hairs few inside a short jagged cup; disk flowers (B, $\times$ 3) numerous, yellow; anthers (C, $\times$ 12) with long slender tails at the base, and rather long terminal sterile tips; style branches (D, $\times$ 12) club-shaped; achenes slightly pubescent; flowers in late summer and autumn (family *Compositae*).

The larger flower-heads of this species have sometimes as many as six hundred disk-flowers and up to a hundred ray-flowers; the ray-flowers are unisexual (female) and the disk-flowers bisexual; the latter bear the anthers and style branches, these possessing hairs directed upwards on the outer side which brush out the pollen as they emerge from the anther-tube. They then spread out horizontally, become recurved and receptive, and receive pollen from other flowers or flower-heads by means of insect visitors. The pollen that is brushed out is largely held by a fringe of hairs on the upper triangular sterile portions of the anthers (see fig. C).

147. Kew-Weed, *Galinsoga parviflora* Cav. (× ⅖); a rather strong-growing annual, an escape from cultivation and now naturalised in many places; stems smooth, branched; leaves opposite, the lower stalked, ovate, acute, 3-nerved from the base, not hairy, bluntly toothed (crenate-dentate); upper leaves becoming sessile and much narrower; flower-heads (A, × 1¼) few, small, with a small green involucre or bracts, the larger bracts opposite the white shortly tubular 3-lobed ray-flowers (B, × 3); disk-flowers (C, × 3) yellow; ovary of ray (female) flowers

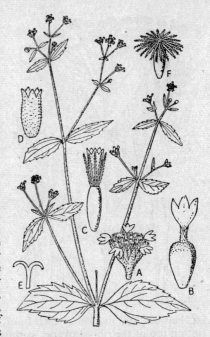

slightly pubescent, becoming black when ripe; corolla of the disk-flowers (D, × 4) 5-lobed, hairy; style branches (E, × 12) of these blunt at the ends; ripe achenes (F, × 3) topped by a spreading series of flat hairy bristles (family *Compositae*).

This is a very interesting alien plant. It was introduced from Peru into the Royal Gardens at Kew in 1796, and was first recorded as having escaped and become naturalised between Kew and East Sheen in 1863, hence " Kew Weed," and it soon grew in the neighbourhood as common as groundsel and spread rapidly. Local people were naturally curious as to the name, and converted it into " Gallant Soldiers," and it even became " Soldiers of the Queen." The plant was also introduced into the Paris Botanic Garden in 1785, and from these two sources it has spread all over Europe. The number of ray flowers is reduced to five, which causes the head to look like a single flower with five petals (see also notes under fig. 151)

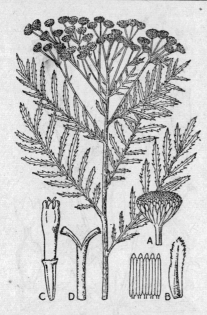

148. Tansy, *Tanacetum vulgare* L. ($\times \frac{2}{3}$); perennial; stems leafy, purplish, closely ribbed; leaves alternate, pinnate, the lobes again deeply cut and often toothed, finely gland-dotted all over; common stalk clasping the stem, ribbed on the back; upper leaves gradually reduced to bracts at the base of the branches of the more or less flat corymb; flower-heads (A, $\times 1\frac{1}{4}$) usually numerous, scented, with 3–4 rows of hairy bracts (B, $\times 4$) with rather jagged edges; flowers (C, $\times 15$) all of one kind, dull yellow, tubular, between 200 and 300 in each head; pappus (calyx) a mere rim on top of the ribbed ovary; corolla with 5 small bladder-like lobes; anthers with barren tops and rounded bases; style branches (D, $\times 25$) very blunt (truncate) and papillous at the apex (family *Compositae*).

The flower-heads of this species are arranged more or less in one plane so that insect visitors can creep over all of them without using their wings. A large number of flowers may, therefore, be pollinated at the same time by a single insect. This crowding together of the heads renders them very conspicuous, which would not be the case were they borne singly, for there are no ray-flowers, as in many other members of the family. The style arms are covered at the tips with a dense bunch of short hairs which brush out the pollen from the anther-tube; they then spread out over the top of the corolla and become receptive for pollen from other flowers or flower-heads. All parts of the plant are bitter and acrid and avoided by stock as a rule. Cattle have been poisoned by it.

149. Mugwort, *Artemisia vulgaris* L. ($\times \frac{2}{5}$); perennial on roadsides and waste places, rank growing to about 3 ft. and flowering in late summer and autumn; stems ribbed, pubescent; leaves (A, $\times \frac{2}{5}$) alternate, twice pinnately lobed, green above, white with a coat of woolly hairs beneath; flower heads very numerous in a terminal leafy panicle, the leaves gradually reduced to bracts; involucral bracts few, cottony-white; flowers in each head of two kinds, the outer female (B, $\times$ 6) with a narrow corolla, a bilobed smooth style and a smooth ovary with rim-like pappus (calyx); the inner (C, $\times$ 6) bisexual with the corolla bell-shaped at

the top, anthers (D, $\times$ 10) with sharp barren tips and sagittate bases, and style branches (E, $\times$ 10) very blunt (truncate) and papillous at the tip (family *Compositae*).

The group or tribe of the family to which *Artemisia* belongs is very interesting because the flowers are *anemophilous*, i.e. their pollen is carried by the wind from flower-head to flower-head or from one plant to another. The individual flowers are very small and inconspicuous, and the flower-heads are often pendulous and therefore do not provide a suitable landing-place for insects; and they secrete no nectar. Where the plant is common it may be the cause of hay fever to those who suffer from this complaint. A closely related genus *Ambrosia* is the cause of much hay-fever in the Eastern United States of America.

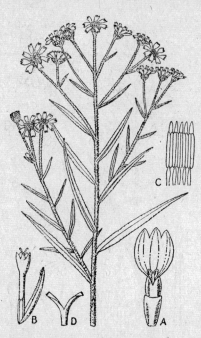

150. Sneezewort Yarrow, *Achillea ptarmica* L. ($\times \frac{2}{3}$); perennial with slender rootstock and erect stems up to 2 ft.; leaves linear, acute, margined with very small close sharp teeth like a fine saw; flower-heads several in a loose terminal cluster and at the ends of the branches, about $\frac{3}{4}$ in. diam.; involucral bracts about 3-seriate, woolly-pubescent, with thinner brown margins; axis of the head furnished with a bract below each flower; rayflowers (A, $\times$ 2) usually about 8, white, with a very broad 3-toothed blade; diskflowers (B, $\times$ 4) greenish-white; anthers (C, $\times$ 10) rounded at the base, and with large barren oblong tips; style-branches (D, $\times$ 8) very blunt, papillous at the ends; achenes flattened and short, without a pappus (family *Compositae*).

This species has larger heads than *A. millefolium* (fig. 151) and there are more ray-flowers. But not so many of the heads are grouped together, so the two species are about equally conspicuous when in flower. Wherever the two grow in abundance they are almost equally common, flower at the same time, and are visited by the same insects. The plant was formerly used in some localities for making tea, and a double form, known as Bachelor's Buttons, is a familiar plant in gardens.

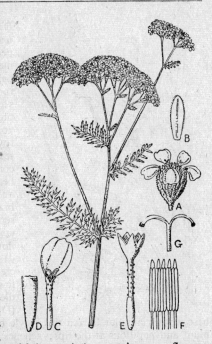

151. Yarrow or Milfoil, *Achillea millefolium* L. ($\times \frac{2}{3}$); perennial, in pastures, meadows and waste places, with creeping under-ground rootstock and numerous short leafy flowerless shoots; flowering stems about 1 ft. high, erect, ribbed; basal leaves pinnately and finely cut into narrow segments which are also deeply divided, lobes ending in a fine point; stem-leaves gradually decreasing upwards; flower-heads (A, $\times$ 3) white or pink, numerous, small, densely arranged in flat corymbs, the side branches often longest; involucral bracts (B, $\times$ 5) in 3-4 series, green up the middle and with brown hairy margins; ray-flowers (C, $\times$ 5) usually 5 (thus resembling a simple flower), female, the corolla with a broad blade 3-toothed at the apex; tube glandular; achene ("seed") (D, $\times$ 4) with a mere rim at the top, smooth; disk-flowers (E, $\times$ 6) tubular, bisexual, upper part bell-shaped, tube glandular; anthers (F, $\times$ 10) with a barren tip and rounded base; style-branches (G, $\times$ 10) papillous at the tip; flowers all summer (family *Compositae*).

The ray-flowers of the individual heads are usually not more than five, each head, therefore, mimicking a single flower with five petals, a very interesting biological feature, as pointed out in the description of *Galinsoga* (fig. 147), in which the same reduction in number has taken place. But plants, like proprietors of fêtes, often gain on the swings what they lose on the roundabouts, and in this case the smallness of the heads is compensated for by their crowding together into a conspicuous flat corymb.

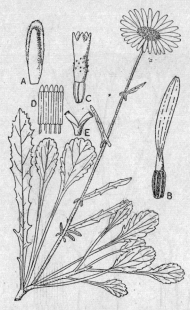

152. Ox-eye or Dog-Daisy, *Chrysanthemum leucanthemum* L. ($\times \frac{2}{5}$); perennial in pastures, meadows, cultivated fields, roadsides, etc.; radical leaves spoon-shaped (spathulate), bluntly toothed, 3-nerved; stem leaves narrowly oblong to linear, sessile, eared at the base, coarsely toothed; flower-heads on long stalks, about 1½–2 in. diam.; bracts (A, $\times$ 2) in 4–5 series, with membranous jagged margins; ray-flowers (B, $\times$ 1½) white; disk-flowers (C, $\times$ 2) creamy yellow, with a few glands near the middle of the tube; anthers (D, $\times$ 6) rounded at the base, with triangular barren tips; style branches (E, $\times$ 8) very blunt and papillous at the tips; achenes blackish, with several lighter coloured ribs, without pappus (family *Compositae*).

This is one of the most handsome members of the Composite family in the British flora, and to be found in pastures and hay-fields. The size of the plant and flower-heads varies much according to soil and situation. For example at the Lizard, where it is exposed to the winds off the sea, the plant is reduced almost to the size of the common Daisy. Nectar rises into the bell of the disk flowers, and in the first stage of flowering pollen is pushed up from the anther-tube by the brush on the ends of the style-arms. Visiting insects then transfer it to the stigmas of other flowers which are in the second stage of development.

153. Scentless Matricary, *Matricaria inodora* L. (× ⅖); erect or spreading branched annual with numerous barren shoots; branches long and forming a loose corymb; leaves 2–3 times pinnate, cut up into very narrow or thread-like segments right to the base of the common axis, glabrous; flower-heads large, on terminal peduncles; bracts of the involucre in several rows, nearly of equal length and with brown jagged margins; ray flowers (A, × 3) numerous, white, ½–¾ in. long, 4–5-nerved; disk-flowers (B, × 3) very numerous, yellow, arranged on a convex or ovoid receptacle (axis) which does

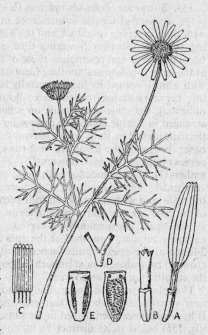

not elongate or enlarge as in the nearly related *M. chamomilla* L.; style (D, × 4) arms truncate; achenes (E, × 4) thickly ribbed on one side and with two glandular spots like little eyes at the top; pappus a narrow almost entire rim (family *Compositae*).

This plant is easily mistaken for *Anthemis cotula* L., in the flower-heads of which, however, there is a bract below each flower on the receptacle; the pair of glands on one side at the top of the achene (see fig. E) is a good spotting feature. A seaside form of the plant with thicker more fleshy leaves is sometimes called var. *maritima*.

A third species which is introduced is a common weed on roadsides and on pathways which it sometimes covers completely. This is *Matricaria matricarioides* (Less.) Porter, a very dwarf plant with no ray-flowers, and yellowish-green disk-flowers.

BUTTERBUR, *Petasites hybridus* (L.) Gaertn.

154. Butterbur, *Petasites hybridus* (L.) Gaertn. (A, male plant, × ½; B, part of female inflorescence in fruit, × ½); perennial with thick creeping rootstock and thickish roots; leaves appearing with or just after flowering time, more or less orbicular, becoming large and resembling those of rhubarb, widely cordate at the base, lobulate and toothed (dentate) on the margin, coated with whitish cobwebby hairs especially below, and easily rubbed off; nerves radiating from the base; flower-heads pink to purple, unisexual, the male and female on separate plants (dioecious), arranged in a large spike-like raceme up to 1 ft. long; stalks of the male up to ¾ in. long, with a narrow bract nearly as long as the base; bracts of the involucre in 2 rows, fairly broad, with 3-5 nerves on the back; male flowers (C, × 3) all tubular, with fertile anthers (D, × 6) rounded at both ends; ovary sterile, and pappus very small; female heads (B, × ½) more widely bell-shaped than the male, and with the stalks in fruit becoming longer than those of the male; bracts nearly in a single row, linear-oblong, rounded at the apex, conspicuously 3-nerved; flowers (E, × 2) very narrowly tubular, 4-toothed at the apex; style (F, × 5) shortly 2-lobed at the apex; fruits (achenes) slightly angular, smooth, crowned by a white almost smooth pappus nearly twice as long as the corolla (family *Compositae*).

This plant grows in damp sandy places and on clay, usually near streams, and when in leaf very much resembles rhubarb. It has sometimes been placed in the same genus as the Coltsfoot (fig. 155) but is quite distinct by its flower-heads, being usually quite unisexual and arranged in large spike-like racemes on different plants. Sometimes the male flower-heads have a few thread-like female flowers around the outside, and occasionally the females have a few males in the middle, which tends to show that this plant has descended from a stock in which the flowers were bisexual. The large leaves of the butterbur cause a dense shade all through the summer, and for this reason few plants are able to grow amongst it. It is rare north of the Forth and Clyde. A closely related cultivated and sometimes naturalised species is the Winter Heliotrope, *Petasites fragrans* L., but with much smaller leaves and fragrant flowers. This flowers earlier than the Butterbur, sometimes in favourable seasons just after Christmas.

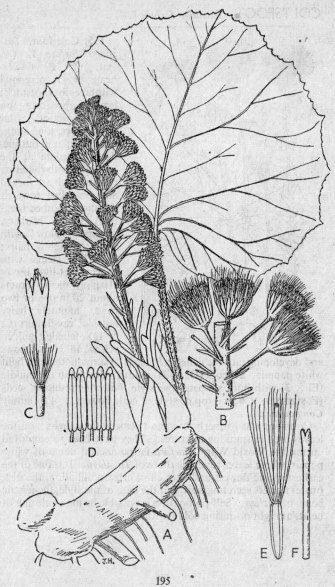

C

D

B

A

J.H.

E F

195

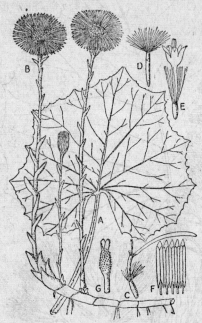

155. Coltsfoot, *Tussilago farfara* L. (A, leaf, × $\frac{2}{5}$; B, flower-heads, × $\frac{2}{5}$); perennial with creeping rootstock; leaves appearing on separate shoots after the flowers, long-stalked, orbicular in outline, deeply cordate at the base, and with radiating nerves which are forked and branched towards the short toothed (dentate) lobes, leathery, covered below with white cobwebby hairs; flowering stems with short bract-like leaves clasping them; bracts about 20 in one or two rows, minutely hairy outside; ray-flowers (C, × 1$\frac{1}{5}$) female, golden yellow, in 3 or 4 rows and developing into the achenes ("seeds") surmounted by a light white pappus; achenes (D, × 3) smooth; flowers in the middle (E, × 3) with both stamens and style, but not producing seeds (F, stamens, × 6; G, top of style of male flowers, × 12) (family *Compositae*).

Coltsfoot was formerly used as a remedy for coughs, and the leaves used in smoking mixtures. They have been so employed during the World War. *Farfara* is the ancient name of white poplar, whose leaves resemble those of *Tussilago*. It is one of the earliest spring flowers and bees effect cross-pollination, the disk (male) flowers secreting nectar at the base of the style, the female being nectarless. Self-pollination is possible owing to closing of heads at night or during cold weather.

156. Oxford Ragwort, *Senecio squalidus* L. ($\times \frac{2}{5}$); annual or biennial much resembling the common Groundsel (figure 158), but with conspicuous ray flowers; leaves all on the stem, with the base half-clasping it and ear-shaped, pinnately and deeply lobed, the lobes narrow and acutely toothed (denticulate), quite glabrous; flower-heads few to numerous, more or less elevated to the same level, about $\frac{3}{4}$ in. diam., the stalks with a few scattered small bracts; involucre (A, $\times \frac{4}{5}$) of two rows of bracts, the outer ones quite small and usually black, the inner about $\frac{1}{4}$ in. long, and mostly with black tips (B, $\times 1\frac{3}{4}$); ray-flowers (C, $\times 2$) 15–20, bright yellow, the blade about $\frac{1}{3}$ in. long; achenes minutely hairy, with a white slightly rough pappus; disk flowers (D, $\times 2$) numerous, yellow; anthers (E, $\times 10$) rounded at both ends, with a triangular membranous tip; style-arms (F, $\times 10$) very blunt, with a tuft of short hairs at the tip; ripe achenes (G, $\times 2$) closely ribbed and minutely hairy, crowned with the white pappus; receptacle (H, $\times 2\frac{1}{2}$) honey-combed, the bracts abruptly reflexed after fruiting (family *Compositae*).

When out of flower this species, an alien from South Europe, might be mistaken for the common Groundsel. It is well established in many districts, especially on walls and embankments in the vicinity of railway stations. It was first established at Oxford and Bideford. A striking feature is the black tips to the bracts of the involucre, and the large ray flowers. In the Groundsel (figure 158) there are normally no ray-flowers.

157. Ragwort, *Senecio jacobaea* L. ($\times \frac{2}{5}$); perennial with a short thick rootstock; stems up to about 4 ft. high or even a little higher in suitable soil, branched only in the upper part, the numerous flowering heads sometimes forming a wide corymb; basal leaves of the first year (A, $\times \frac{2}{5}$) deeply and irregularly pinnately lobed with the end lobe the largest and less divided, all coarsely lobulate and toothed, minutely scurfy pubescent on both surfaces, especially on the nerves; stem leaves sessile and much divided; flowerheads usually very many, on slender, somewhat woolly stalks, $\frac{1}{2}-\frac{3}{4}$ in. diam.; involucral bracts (B, $\times$ 3) in one main series with a few extra smaller ones at the base, with rather thin edges and often darker coloured tops; ray-flowers (C, $\times 2\frac{1}{2}$) yellow, about 15–20, spreading, with glabrous achenes; disk-flowers (D, $\times 2\frac{1}{2}$) numerous, with shortly pubescent achenes and a longer more copious pappus; anthers (E, $\times$ 8) slightly ear-shaped at the base; style-arms (F, $\times$ 8) very blunt, with a brush of thick short hairs at the apex (family *Compositae*).

A common and quite handsome species in pastures and on road-sides; usually avoided by stock and often left standing in closely cropped fields, but has been eaten by sheep in this country without any harmful effects; in other countries, however, regarded as dangerous. This species may be at once distinguished from amongst others closely resembling it, such as *S. aquaticus* Huds., and *S. erucifolius* L., in having two kinds of achenes, those of the ray flowers being glabrous and of the disk hairy.

158. Groundsel, *Senecio vulgaris* L. ($\times \frac{2}{5}$); annual herb up to about a foot high, with a finely fibrous root; stems succulent, glabrous or thinly clothed with rather long cottony hairs; leaves alternate, sessile and half clasping the stem, pinnately lobed and irregularly dentate, succulent, not hairy or only slightly so when young; flower-heads (A, $\times 1\frac{1}{2}$) few, in close terminal and axillary corymbs; involucre narrowly bell-shaped, with one principal row of bracts and several very small black-tipped bracts at the base;

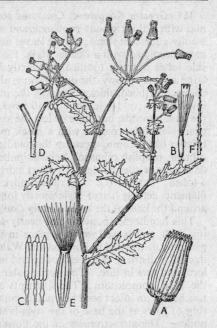

longer row of bracts forming a tube; flowers (florets) (B, $\times 1\frac{1}{2}$) all of one kind, yellow, no ray flowers (or very rarely a few small ones present); pappus of many slender white toothed (barbellate) bristles (F, $\times 6$); corolla tubular, 5-lobed; ovary minutely hairy; anthers (C, $\times 5$) rounded at the base and with produced barren tips; style-branches (D, $\times 5$) very blunt, with short club-shaped hairs (papillae) at the tips; achene (fruit) (E, $\times 5$) with longitudinal ribs, not hairy (family *Compositae*).

Groundsel needs no introduction, being a " noxious " weed of cultivation in temperate regions. It has its uses, however, being a good rabbit and cage-bird food-plant. The flowers contain nectar which ascends into the upper bell-shaped part of the corolla. But insect visitors are few, and automatic self-pollination regularly takes place. It has been shown, however, that cross-fertilised seeds produce larger and more fertile plants.

159. Greater Knapweed, *Centaurea scabiosa* L. ($\times \frac{1}{3}$); perennial with a thick woody rootstock and with hard ribbed rather woolly-pubescent stems; all the leaves pinnately lobed, the basal more deeply so with a slender stalk, the stem leaves sessile, the side lobes coarsely toothed or shortly lobulate; flower-heads large and very showy, the outer flowers always larger and sterile; peduncles ribbed, thicker towards the involucre; bracts of the involucre (A, $\times 1\frac{1}{2}$) in about 8–10 rows, gradually larger from the base upwards, but more or less the same shape and narrowly triangular to lanceolate, with a black margin and fringed with bristles like a comb, green up the middle; flowers (B, $\times 2$) all tubular, purplish crimson; achenes pubescent; pappus of stiff, flat, white bristles bordered by short hairs; corolla rather deeply 5-lobed; anthers (C, $\times 4$) rather thick and forming a cone; filaments densely hairy; style shortly lobed, with a ring of hairs around the base of the lobes (family *Compositae*).

This handsome species is not nearly so common as *C. nigra* (fig. 160), and is well worth a place in a flower garden. It is generally distributed in England and Wales, being more common in chalky districts, but does not extend far into Scotland, and is local and rare in Eire. The sterile outer flowers serve to render the head conspicuous. The filaments are irritable and when touched by an insect bend and pull down the anther cylinder, the ring of hairs at the base of the style-branches brushing out the pollen. The attractiveness of the flower heads is very greatly enhanced by the neutral outer flowers, which in a way mimic the ray-flowers of other members of the family. That this is their function seems clear, because they have no bell for the storage of nectar, which is confined to the bisexual flowers. The genus is readily recognised amongst British members of the family by the comb-like structure of the involucral bracts. It is very richly represented in species in the Mediterranean and Caucasus regions, and many handsome species are grown in our gardens.

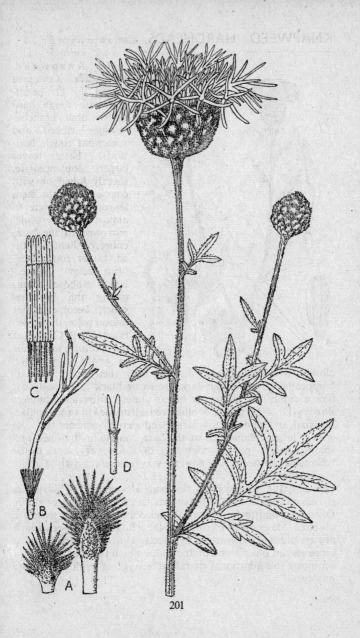

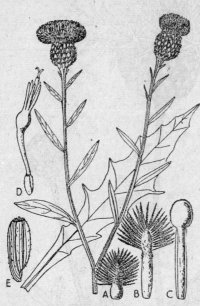

160. K n a p w e e d,
Hardheads, *Centaurea
nigra* L. ($\times \frac{2}{5}$); perennial with tough hard
stems and branches
strongly ribbed and
somewhat rough (sca-
brid); basal leaves
larger, oblanceolate,
shortly lobed or with
coarse teeth, the stem
leaves oblanceolate to
almost linear, sessile,
narrowed to the base,
entire, or slightly toothed, rather rough (sca-
brid) below; flower-
heads globose, termi-
nating the branches
which become rather
thicker below the heads;
bracts (A, B, C, $\times$ 2) of
the involucre numerous
in about 6–8 rows,
closely overlapping and showing only their upper part or
"appendage," the latter dark brown or black and deeply cut
like a comb, the innermost bracts almost entire and shining;
flowers (D, $\times 1\frac{1}{2}$) purple or bluish red, all of one kind and tubular,
bisexual, or the outer row larger and sterile; achenes (E, $\times$ 4)
with a large oblique scar at the base, longitudinally lined and
slightly hairy; pappus consisting of a few very short teeth;
receptacle between the flowers very densely bristly (family
Compositae).

A common plant in fields, flowering all summer. This species
is remarkable in that it sometimes has a row of larger sterile
flowers around the outside of the head and sometimes these are
absent. Many other species have these larger ray flowers, which
are an additional attraction to insects, so that *C. nigra* seems to
represent an older stock of the genus which is in the process of
acquiring this additional character, a stage of evolution before
our eyes !

161. Spear Thistle, *Cirsium lanceolatum* (L.) Scop. ($\times \frac{2}{5}$); biennial up to about 4 ft. high; stem continuously winged and armed with long pointed very sharp prickles, ribbed and rather woolly hairy like the lower surface of the leaves; basal leaves elongated but less prickly than the stem leaves, the latter rather narrowly lanceolate, decurrent on the stem and forming the wing, deeply pinnately lobed, the lobes ending in a very long and very sharp prickle with much smaller prickles between them; upper surface loosely clothed

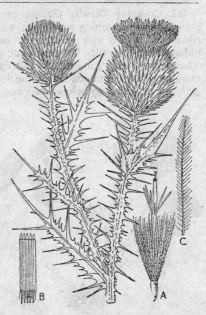

with very short bristly hairs, woolly below with whitish hairs; flower heads rather large, few, stalked or sometimes subsessile and about 3 in a cluster, about 1¾ in. long when in flower; involucre broadly campanulate, composed of very numerous bracts in about 10–15 rows, all narrow and ending in a long sharp hard prickle, and with a hard nearly glabrous basal portion; flowers all alike (A, × 1¼), very numerous, bright purple, bisexual; corolla-tube long and slender, with narrow lobes; anthers (B, × 2) with tails at the base; achenes glabrous; pappus (C, × 2½) very copious, feathery (family *Compositae*).

This species is common in fields, pastures and waste places and is a nuisance to the farmer when once it gets established, as the heads mature rapidly and the achenes (" seeds ") are blown about by the wind. Being a biennial it is more easily eradicated, however, than the Creeping Thistle, especially if cut before flowering. Long-tongued bees visit the flowers for the nectar concealed at the base of the very long corolla-tube.

162. Creeping Thistle, *Cirsium arvense* (L.) Scop. (× ⅖); perennial with creeping rootstock; stems annual, erect, leafy, ribbed and prickly with the decurrent bases of the leaves; leaves oblanceolate in outline but deeply and undulately lobed, woolly when young, embracing the stem at the base, the very prickly margins often continued down the latter for some distance, glabrous or nearly so below when mature; flower-heads rather

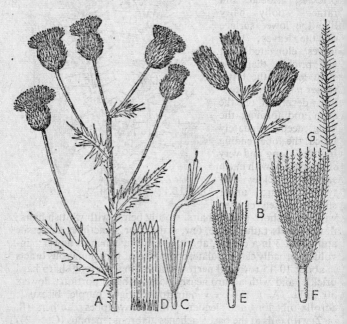

small, few in a lax terminal corymb, unisexual, the males (A) on one plant, the females (B) on another, the males nearly globose with very projecting rose-purple or rarely white flowers (C, × 2½) and conspicuous anthers (D), the females narrower and with longer bracts but shorter flowers (E, × 2½) with conspicuous stigmas, and the pappus soon a prominent feature, both kinds of heads with numerous rows of narrow bracts with short spiny tips; pappus feathery (i.e. with long side hairs); achenes ("seeds") (F, × 2½) quite smooth (family *Compositae*).

A very common Thistle in cultivated and waste places.

163. Cat's-ear, *Hypochaeris radicata* L. (× ⅔); strong growing perennial with a Dandelion-like rootstock; stems erect, leafless, up to 2 ft. high, simple or branched into 2 or 3 peduncles; leaves all from the rootstock, spreading, oblanceolate in outline, pinnately lobulate with spreading or slightly recurved lobules, clothed on both surfaces with rather stiff hairs (hispid); midrib broad; lateral nerves slender and inconspicuous; peduncles smooth, with here and there a small bract; flower head pale yellow, about 1⅛ in. diam.; bracts of the involucre in about 3 rows, the outer (A, × 1¼) short and lanceolate with a row of bristles up the middle, the innermost (B, × 1¼) as long as the flowers and smooth on the back, long-pointed; flowers (C, × 2) all of one kind, as in the Dandelion; achene smooth; pappus small in the flower, consisting of slender bristles with long side hairs (plumose); corolla-tube slender spreading out into a 5-toothed blade; anther cone erect, slender, with the stigmas at length protruding, the base of the anthers with long tails (D, × 5); ripe achenes (E, × 3) closely tuberculate and all narrowed into a long slender beak with the spreading plumose pappus at the top (family *Compositae*).

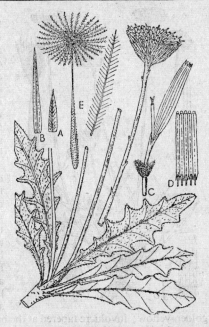

This rather rank growing Dandelion-like plant occurs in meadows, pastures, road-sides and waste places, and flowers in summer and autumn. It is easily distinguished from the Dandelion (fig. 166) by the long lateral hairs on the pappus-bristles. In the closely related but less common *Hypochaeris glabra* L., the outer achenes have no beak, and the leaves are glabrous.

AUTUMN HAWKBIT, *Leontodon autumnalis* L.

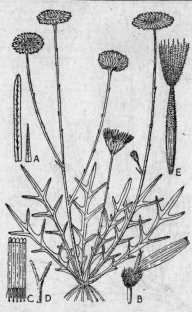

164. Autumn Hawkbit, *Leontodon autumnalis* L. ($\times \frac{2}{5}$); perennial and very like a small dandelion in general appearance; leaves all from the root, spreading, rather deeply pinnately lobed, having a narrow blade and spreading linear side-lobes, glabrous or with a few long stiff hairs on the midrib below; flowering stems leafless or nearly so, simple or with a few branches in the upper part, the branches with a small bract at the base, and bearing here and there a few, short subulate-lanceolate bracts; heads about $\frac{3}{4}$–1 in. diam., golden-yellow; involucre tapered at the base into the stalk, with one main whorl of long narrow bracts setose along the middle, and a much shorter outer series more or less subulate (A, $\times$ 2); flowers (B, $\times$ 1$\frac{3}{4}$) all of one kind (bisexual) and ligulate, having both stamens and style with fertile ovary; corolla minutely 5-toothed at the apex; anthers (C, $\times$ 4) tailed at the base; style-arms hairy outside (D, $\times$ 4); achene (E, $\times$ 4) narrowed to the top but not beaked, minutely tuberculate in the upper half and microscopically reticulate all over, brown when ripe; pappus feathery (family *Compositae*).

Grows in meadows, pastures and waste ground, flowering in summer and autumn; the heads expand in the sunshine and form a golden-yellow disk up to an inch in diameter, but contract to very small dimensions during rainy weather; either cross-pollination by insects or self-pollination occurs. The floral structure is very similar to that of Cats-ear, *Hypochaeris radicata* L. (fig. 163), but the heads are more dainty and the achenes lack the long beak of that species.

165. Smooth Crepis, *Crepis capillaris* (L.) Wallr. (× ⅖); an erect branched annual or biennial, up to 3 ft. high; stem with few scattered leaves, green or purplish, glabrous or hairy towards the base; basal leaves long and narrow, up to about 9 in. long, rather irregularly and pinnately lobed and toothed, tapered to and sheathing at the base of the stalk; stem leaves (when present) sessile, linear, markedly arrow-shaped (sagittate) at the base, sometimes with rather long narrow spreading or slightly recurved side-lobes; flower-heads rather small for a kind of hawkweed or dandelion, erect in bud, few together in irregular corymbs or rarely solitary according to vigour of growth; peduncles with a rather small linear bract at the base; bracts of the involucre in 2 distinct rows, an outer row of few very narrow short bracts, and an inner row of linear erect bracts slightly glandular-hairy on the outside, closing up and becoming conical in fruit; flowers (A, × 2) yellow, all of one kind, with both stamens and style; achenes (B, × 3) closely ribbed when ripe, not contracted into a beak; pappus pure white, soft and silky, though minutely roughened (barbellate) (C, × 10) (family *Compositae*).

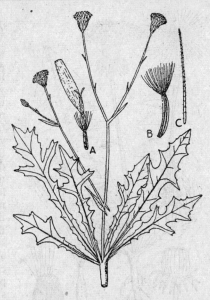

Except for *Lapsana* (fig. 170) in which there is no pappus, and for species of *Lactuca* (which have beaked achenes) this species has the smallest flower-heads of any British plant of the Hawkweed or Dandelion type, and with the aid of the figure and description will probably be recognised. It is common in fields, dry banks, roadsides and waste places, and it flowers the whole summer and well into the autumn.

166. Dandelion, *Taraxacum officinale* Weber (aggregate) ($\times \frac{2}{5}$); a perennial herb and troublesome weed in fields, lawns and waste places, with a thick tap-root, full of milky juice; leaves all from the root (radical) very variable, from entire or nearly so to deeply pinnate-lobed, the lobes triangular or lanceolate and usually more or less recurved, the terminal one often the largest; flower-head stalks (peduncles) up to about a foot high according to soil and exposure, without small subsidiary bracts hollow; involucre (A, $\times \frac{2}{5}$) double, the outer bracts abruptly reflexed, the inner erect, glabrous; flowers (B, $\times 2$) numerous in the head, bright golden yellow, all bisexual and fertile; achenes at first shortly beaked, at length with a very long beak (C, $\times 2\frac{1}{2}$) topped by a spreading pappus of smooth silky white hairs; body of achene with short sharp points; corolla-tube not hairy, the limb (blade) with 5 teeth at the top; all the achenes at length fall from the receptacle, with the bracts reflexed (D, $\times \frac{2}{5}$) (family *Compositae*).

Like the Daisy, the Dandelion is known to everybody. It is a very variable plant according to soil and situation, and some botanists prefer to regard the various forms, few of which are constant, as distinct species, and a great number have been described in consequence. This genus, like the Brambles (*Rubus*), and Roses (*Rosa*), is still evolving rapidly.

167. Prickly Sow-thistle, *Sonchus asper* (L.) Hill ($\times \frac{2}{5}$); an annual with a rosette of radical leaves, usually a foot or two high; stems hollow and succulent, with white milk-like juice, often tinged with crimson, glabrous but often covered with a fine bloom; basal leaves more or less spoon-shaped, with an obovate upper portion and a long tapered lower part, closely and very sharply toothed, the teeth unequal-sized and spreading at a right angle, often tinged with crimson; stem leaves sessile, oblong-lanceolate, markedly ear-shaped at the base and embracing the

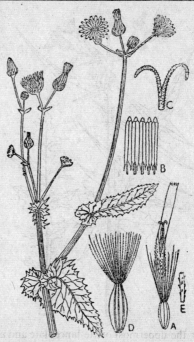

stem, with sharp prickly spreading teeth, dark green above, often with a purplish midrib; flower-heads in an irregular corymb, the end clusters subumbellate, becoming conical and pointed after flowering; bracts in about 3 rows, the outermost much the shortest, rather broad and pointed; flowers (A, $\times 1\frac{3}{4}$) pale yellow, strap-shaped, all of one kind, with a narrow tubular base hairy in the upper part, with 5 sharp teeth at the apex of the limb; anthers (B, $\times 6$) united into a tube with tails at the base, and with black tops; achene (seed) (D, $\times 4$) flattened, brown, with parallel ribs; pappus of many slender white slightly roughened hairs (E, $\times 10$); style branches hairy (C, $\times 6$) (family *Compositae*).

This is a common weed and is closely related to *Sonchus oleraceus* L., the Smooth Sowthistle, which is much less prickly with the basal lobes of the stem-leaves spreading in the same plane as the rest of the blade. The achenes of *S. oleraceus* are covered with short prickles.

168. Common Sowthistle, *Sonchus olera-ceus* L. ($\times \frac{2}{5}$); an annual with a rather thick hollow stem, up to about 4 ft. high, glabrous all over except a few scattered stalked glands towards the top of the main flower head stalk; basal leaves (A, $\times \frac{2}{5}$) rather irregularly pinnately divided almost to the middle, lobes narrowly triangular and sharply and irregularly toothed; stem leaves sessile, clasping the stem with long often very acute earlike bases (auricles), deeply pin-nately lobed like the basal leaves or less lob-ed and with a large ter-minal triangular lobe, or the uppermost ovate-lanceolate and at most coarsely dentate; flower-heads subumbellate above the last leafy bract, in the axils of the stalks often little balls of woolly hairs; involucral bracts in about 3 rows, the outermost much shorter, glabrous or with a few stiff hairs outside; flowers all of one kind, ligulate, the blade toothed at the top; achenes with slender ribs when ripe, glabrous; pappus white, smooth (family *Compositae*).

As mentioned under *Sonchus asper* (fig. 167), this species is not at all prickly, the leaf-teeth being sharp but not pungent. It is the more common species, being also a weed of cultivation, and widely distributed over the world. Frequently the two species are found growing together.

169. Mouse-Ear Hawkweed, *Hieracium pilosella* L. ($\times \frac{1}{2}$); rootstock perennial with spreading tufts of radical leaves, with creeping offshoots bearing smaller narrow spoon-shaped leaves, rather densely clothed with long slender and very short white hairs; leaves oblanceolate, tapered to the base, not toothed, green above and loosely covered with long stiff bulbous-based hairs (A, $\times$ 7), woolly tomentose below with white star-shaped hairs (B, $\times$ 7); flower-head stalks arising from among the leaves, usually up to about 6 in. high, clothed with very short star-shaped hairs and longer gland-tipped hairs (C, $\times$ 2); involucral bracts

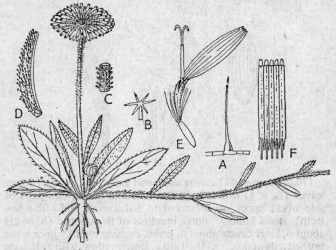

(D, $\times$ 2½) in 2-3 rows, broadly linear, with a thin membranous margin, covered outside with short stiff blackish often gland-tipped hairs and an under layer of minute star-shaped hairs; flowers (E, $\times$ 2) all of one kind, ligulate, lemon yellow above, often tinged with dull crimson below, 5-toothed at the apex; anthers with long tails at the base (F, $\times$ 5); pappus white, slightly rough; achenes smooth, rather short (family *Compositae*).

This is a very distinctive plant and the most easily recognised of this large and puzzling genus. Perhaps in no other is there so little unanimity of opinion amongst botanists with regard to the number of species.

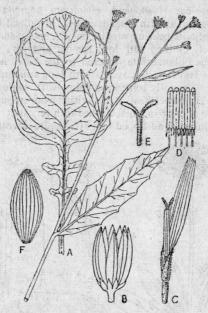

170. Nipplewort, *Lapsana communis* L. ($\times \frac{2}{5}$); annual; lower leaves (A, $\times \frac{2}{5}$) with a large end lobe and one or two pairs of side-lobes; upper leaves lanceolate, not stalked, and with a few teeth; stems hollow; outer bractlets of flower-head (B, $\times 2\frac{1}{4}$) about 6, inner bracts about 8, green, exuding a milky juice when bruised; flowers (C, $\times 4$) all alike, lemon yellow, with 5 stamens (D, $\times 8$) united in a tube around the hairy style (E, $\times 8$); anthers tailed; fruits ("seeds") (F, $\times 3$) closely lined with greenish nerves, but without a pappus (family *Compositae*).

A common weed by roadsides and in waste and cultivated places, flowering from late summer until late autumn. The common name refers to its former reputed use in curing sore nipples. The flowers in the heads are all of one kind, i.e. with male and female organs in the same flower. In each head there are up to about 18 flowers which open between 6 and 7 a.m., closing again at 10 or 11 a.m. (normal time). In bad weather they remain closed, when self-pollination may take place.

171. Black Nightshade, *Solanum nigrum* L. (× ⅔); annual or biennial up to a foot or so in height, stem much branched, glabrous or minutely hairy; leaves alternate, more or less ovate or rhomboid-ovate, narrowed at the base into the winged stalk, with a few coarse blunt teeth or short lobes; flowers small, drooping, in an umbel-like stalked cluster remote from the axils of the leaves, usually from the upper part of the internode; no bracts; calyx (A, × ⅘) 5-lobed to about the middle; corolla (B, × ⅘) white, with a short tube and 5 triangular lobes at length

reflexed and shortly hairy on the margin; stamens (C, × 2½) 5, inserted in the throat of the corolla, and alternate with the lobes, the anthers connivent and forming a little cone covering the mouth of the corolla-tube, each opening by two terminal holes (pores); ovary (D, × 2½) 2-locular; style short; berries fleshy, drooping, small, globose, usually black or green, rarely pale yellow or red, containing numerous flattened almost orbicular minutely pitted seeds (family *Solanaceae*).

This is a weed widely spread nearly all over the world, and flowers and fruits all summer and autumn. The flowers do not secrete nectar, but provide pollen for insect visitors. They hang downwards and close at night. Considering the small size of the flower the anthers are large and connivent in a cone with the stigma protruding a little beyond, so that self-pollination is easy, the pollen falling out through the terminal pores of the anthers. The plant is poisonous, but varies in toxicity according to soil.

172. Bittersweet, *Solanum dulcamara* L. ($\times \frac{2}{5}$); perennial, woody at the base, with straggling branches several feet long and clinging to hedges; branches very softly and shortly hairy or sometimes with only a few stiffer hairs; leaves alternate, the lower often deeply 3-lobed, with a large ovate middle and two small side lobes; upper leaves ovate, cordate at the base, pointed at the apex, softly to thinly hairy below when mature, rather densely so when young, margins entire; flowers (A, $\times 1\frac{3}{4}$) in small panicles, the common stalk placed opposite to the leaf (leaf-opposed);

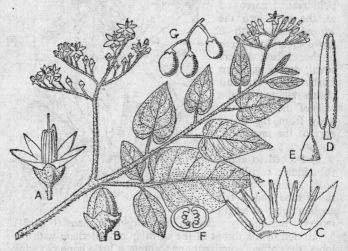

stalks hairy; calyx with 5 short broad lobes; corolla (C, $\times 1\frac{3}{4}$) blue, marked with violet veins, with a short tube and 5 spreading lobes which do not overlap in bud (B, $\times 1\frac{3}{4}$), the latter shortly hairy outside; stamens (D, $\times 4$) 5, alternating with the lobes, the anthers standing up in a cone around the style, large and opening by a pore at the top; ovary (E, $\times 3$) above the corolla, 2-locular (F, $\times 6$), style slender, unbranched, exceeding the anthers; fruit (G, $\times 1\frac{1}{4}$) a small globular or ovoid red berry (family *Solanaceae*).

Bittersweet is included in the British Pharmaceutical Codex, but is now rarely used in medicine. The drug is prepared from the dried stems and branches. The berries are poisonous, though stock rarely touch the green parts of the plant.

173. Deadly Night-
shade, *Atropa bella-
donna* L. ($\times \frac{2}{5}$); rootstock thick and fleshy;
stem branched, often
dividing into 3, the
whole plant minutely
hairy; leaves in pairs
on one side of the
stem, very unequal-
sized in each pair,
often one hardly half
the size of the other,
ovate or ovate-elliptic,
triangular at the apex,
wedge-shaped at the
base and continued
down the stalk, with
about 5–8 pairs of
widely spreading
arched lateral nerves;
no stipules; flowers

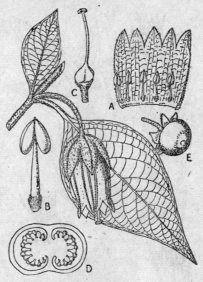

drooping, solitary and placed between the stalks of the two leaves
or in the forks of the stem; stalk about as long as or longer than
the flower; calyx bell-shaped, 5-lobed to about the middle, lobes
triangular-ovate, acute; corolla dull purple tinged with green,
especially near the base, tube bell-shaped, with 5 recurved
rather acute broad lobes; stamens included in the tube and
inserted near the base; style as long as the corolla, with a
rounded head-like green stigma; fruit a purplish black berry
about $\frac{1}{2}$ in. diam., depressed-globose, girt by the persistent
spreading calyx (family *Solanaceae*).

Not a common plant, but included here because of its medicinal
and poisonous properties. All parts are poisonous, especially the
berries. It is usually found in waste places especially amongst
ruins and by roadsides, and flowers in summer. Nectar is
secreted at the base of the ovary and cross-pollination is effected
chiefly by humble bees. The style usually falls off and the corolla
withers about an hour after pollination, so that fertilisation is
very rapid.

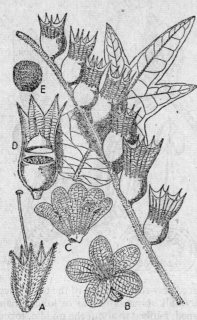

174. Henbane, *Hyoscyamus niger* L. ($\times \frac{3}{5}$); annual herb with an unpleasant odour, more or less hairy and viscid all over; radical leaves large, with short stalks, coarsely and pinnately lobed; stem-leaves alternate, smaller, not stalked, narrowly ovate in outline, with 2 or 3 coarse teeth or short pointed lobes on each margin, hairy especially on the nerves below; flowers numerous, at first crowded amongst the upper leaves and sessile, but spreading out in fruit on one side of the shoot like that of a Borage; calyx (A, $\times \frac{3}{4}$) with a broadly bell-shaped very hairy tube and 5 broad short lobes each ending in a sharp point which hardens and is spine-like in fruit, tube strongly ribbed; corolla (B, $\times \frac{1}{2}$) yellowish white, closely veined with dark purple, and with a purple "eye," lobes rounded and slightly unequal; stamens (C, $\times 1\frac{1}{4}$) 5, with purple anthers; ovary 2-locular, with numerous ovules; fruit (D, $\times \frac{2}{5}$) enclosed in the enlarged markedly ribbed calyx, the upper part of the fruit splitting off like a helmet and thicker and harder than the lower portion; seeds (E, $\times 5$) very numerous (family *Solanaceae*).

Not a common plant, but included here because of its medicinal importance; grows chiefly on rubbish heaps and waste places near habitations, and flowers in summer. The seeds are poisonous, and animals may be affected by them if mixed with fodder.

175. Bindweed, *Convolvulus arvensis* L. ($\times \frac{4}{5}$); perennial with a slender creeping rootstock; stems prostrate or twining up supports to about 2 ft. high, often strangling other plants, twisting spirally, glabrous; leaves alternate, stalked, ovate or oblong-ovate, rounded to a small point at the apex, with spreading lobes at the base (hastate), otherwise with entire margins, glabrous and the nerves rather radiating from the base; flowers usually paired on axillary peduncles, only one of a pair open at the same time, with a small narrow bract at the base of each ultimate stalk (pedicel) and often a pair of small bracts below only one of

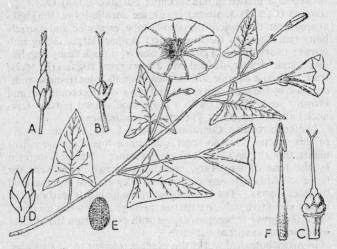

the flowers; calyx (B, $\times \frac{4}{5}$) of 5 rounded free sepals about $\frac{1}{6}$ in. long; corolla pink or nearly white, funnel-shaped, about 1 in. diam., very shallowly 5-lobed, the lobes forming little more than a wavy margin and spreading or slightly recurved; stamens 5, inserted at the base of the corolla; anthers facing outwards; ovary (C, $\times \frac{4}{5}$) 2-locular, each with 2 ovules; fruit (D, $\times \frac{3}{4}$) a small capsule divided into 2 compartments by a thin partition; seeds (E, $\times 3$) minutely pitted (family *Convolvulaceae*).

Though a very beautiful little plant, this is a troublesome weed in cultivation and difficult to eradicate. This is because of its extensive root-system, which may penetrate the soil to a great depth.

176. White Bindweed, *Calystegia sepium* (L.) R.Br. ($\times \frac{1}{2}$); perennial with a creeping rootstock; stems twining and twisting spirally over hedges and bushes; leaves alternate, broadly ovate or ovate-triangular, acutely pointed at the apex, deeply heart-shaped (cordate) and often with angular lobes at the base, not hairy, with several main nerves radiating from the base; flowers axillary, rather long-stalked; calyx enclosed by two large over-lapping green bracts, bell-shaped, 5-lobed; corolla (B, $\times \frac{1}{2}$) large and pure white or with a pink band up the middle of each lobe, bell-shaped, with short spreading-recurved lobes; lobes twisted and plaited in bud (opening out like a fan) (A, $\times \frac{3}{4}$); stamens (C, $\times 2$) 5, alternate with the corolla-lobes, the stalks arising from the base of the corolla-tube, expanded and coarsely hairy (papillous) in the lower part; anthers large, facing out-wards; ovary (D, $\times 2$) girt at the base by a thick fleshy ring-like disk; style slender, divided into 2 corrugated stigmas (E, $\times 7$); fruit a globose capsule, almost membranous, containing 4 seeds, enclosed by the persistent bracts and calyx which become thin and brown; seeds (F, $\times 2$) with a horse-shoe shaped portion (car-uncle) at the base (G, $\times 2$) (family *Convolvulaceae*).

Unlike its relative, *Convolvulus arvensis* L. (fig. 175) the flowers of this species have no scent and remain open on moonlight nights, though they close during wet weather. Nectar is secreted by the base of the ovary, and diurnal hawk-moths visit the flowers. Although very conspicuous they are not much visited by other insects. The broad bases of the filaments surround the nectar and leave only five narrow passages, and when an insect visits the flower it becomes dusted with pollen from the anthers which in this case face outwards.

In many botanical works this plant is referred to *Convolvulus*, but the famous British botanist, Robert Brown, who flourished at the beginning of last century, considered it to be distinct and there are good reasons for upholding this view. It differs from *Convolvulus* by the presence of large leafy bracts which enclose the real calyx.

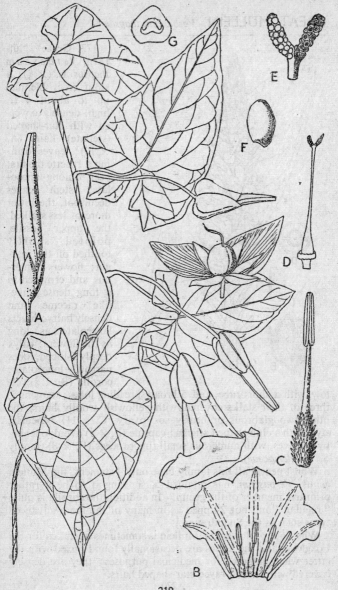

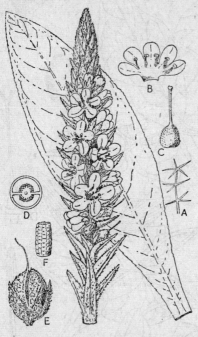

177. Great Mullein, *Verbascum thapsus* L. ($\times \frac{2}{5}$); a stout erect biennial up to about 4 ft. high, densely covered with star-shaped (stellate) hairs (A, $\times$ 10); leaves forming a rosette the first year, oblong-lanceolate; stem leaves decurrent, the lower more or less stalked, the upper sessile, pointed, shortly toothed on the margin; flowers numerous and crowded in a long dense spike-like raceme and densely hairy; bracts lanceolate, as long as the flowers; calyx deeply 5-lobed, lobes narrowly lanceolate; corolla (B, $\times \frac{3}{5}$) yellow, with a short tube, and 5 broad spreading lobes; stamens 5, three of their stalks covered with yellowish woolly hairs, the other two glabrous or nearly so; ovary (C, $\times 1\frac{1}{2}$) 2-locular, style with a club-shaped stigma; capsule (E, $\times \frac{4}{5}$) ovoid, opening by 2 valves, with numerous small rugose seeds (F, $\times$ 8) (family *Scrophulariaceae*).

Whilst nearly all this family have only 4 stamens, the Mullein genus, *Verbascum*, has retained 5, showing it to be a rather primitive member of the group. In addition the corolla is quite "regular" and not 2-lipped as in many of the more advanced types such as the Snapdragon.

When out of flower the Mullein is sometimes mistaken for the Foxglove, and the leaves are occasionally found mixed with the latter when gathered for medicinal purposes; they are densely covered with several-rayed star-shaped hairs.

178. Foxglove, *Digitalis purpurea* L. (× $\frac{2}{5}$); usually a biennial but sometimes persisting a year or two longer; basal leaves on long stalks which are winged with the continued base of the leaf blade, broadly lanceolate, up to a foot or more in length, rather abruptly narrowed into the stalk at the base, toothed on the margin, rather coarsely reticulate-veined, covered with soft white downy hairs below; flowering stems up to about 4 ft. high or higher bearing a few lanceolate leaves which gradually pass into bracts, the latter lanceolate, sessile, entire; flowers numerous in the raceme, drooping, light purple and usually beautifully spotted

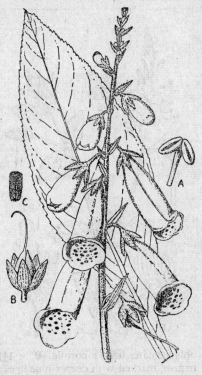

with crimson, rarely white; calyx large, 5-lobed to the base, 4 of the lobes ovate, the fifth (upper) smaller and more pointed; corolla up to 2 in. long, shortly 4-lobed; stamens 4, included; anther-cells (A, × 1½) divergent; ovary 2-locular, with very numerous ovules; style shortly 2-lobed; capsule (B, × $\frac{2}{5}$) with numerous very small minutely honey-combed seeds (C, × 5) (family *Scrophulariaceae*).

Everyone knows this beautiful plant which is well worth a place in the garden. It is official in the British Pharmacopœia, the dried leaves being used in medicine for heart trouble. It has been recognised as poisonous for centuries, one of its common names being Dead Man's Bells! All parts of the plant are poisonous, especially the seeds.

221

GERMANDER SPEEDWELL, BIRD'S-EYE, *Veronica chamaedrys* L.

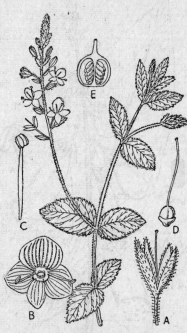

179. Germander Speedwell, Bird's-eye, *Veronica chamaedrys* L. ($\times \frac{3}{5}$); perennial, with several slender stems decumbent and rooting towards the base, then erect or ascending; stems glabrous except for two opposite lines of rather long whitish hairs in line with the leaves; leaves opposite, nearly sessile, ovate, toothed (crenate), with a few bristly fine hairs on the nerves below; the very short stalks margined with long fine hairs; flowers in slender racemes from the upper leaf-axils, the axis or common stalk with fine hairs all around; each flower with a shortly stalked green bract at the base; calyx (A, $\times$ 2) deeply 4-lobed, lobes broadly oblanceolate, hairy; corolla (B, $\times$ 1$\frac{1}{2}$) deep sky blue fading to mauve, marked with deeper blue lines and with a white " eye," the mouth guarded with erect bristly hairs on the lower side, 4-lobed; stamens (C, $\times$ 4) 2, between the back and side lobes of the corolla, long-exserted; filaments and anthers blue; ovary (D, $\times$ 5) rounded, minutely hairy, 2-locular, with a nectariferous ring around the base; style slender, blue; fruit flat, notched at the top (family *Scrophulariaceae*).

The flowers of this plant are very beautiful when seen through a hand-lens. Nectar is secreted in a fleshy disk around the base of the ovary and protected by hairs partly across the mouth of the corolla. The two stamens are lateral and divergent and are seized by an insect alighting on the flower and drawn against its body, on which pollen is deposited and carried to the stigma of another flower.

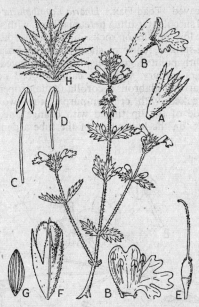

180. Eyebright, *Euphrasia officinalis* L. (aggregate) ($\times \frac{2}{5}$); erect annual with simple stems or much-branched from the base; stems covered with downwardly directed hairs; leaves opposite, small, sessile, ovate in outline but deeply toothed, teeth ending in a fine point; flowers in the axils of the upper leaves, some crowded at the top and forming a rather dense bracteate spike; bracts (H, $\times 2\frac{1}{4}$) rounded, deeply toothed; calyx (A, $\times 2\frac{1}{4}$) 5-lobed to about the middle, lobes acute, hairy; corolla (B, $\times 1\frac{1}{4}$) very variable in colour, white or reddish and streaked with purple, with a yellow spot in the throat; upper lip forming a hood over the anthers and shortly 2-lobed; lower lip 3-lobed, each lobe deeply and widely notched; tube hairy outside; stamens (D, $\times 2\frac{1}{4}$) 4, on the corolla, not protruded, one pair longer than the other, one of the anther-lobes of each of the shorter stamens with a long point at the base, the other bases with short points; ovary (E, $\times 3$) girt by a cupular disk; hairy at the top; style undivided, slender, hairy in the upper part; fruit (F, $\times 3$) clasped by the calyx; seeds (G, $\times 8$) few, pointed at each end, and marked by ridges (family *Scrophulariaceae*).

181. Ivy-Leaved Toad-Flax, *Linaria cymbalaria* (L.) Mill.
($\times \frac{3}{4}$); small succulent trailing perennial herb, with slender stems
rooting at the lower nodes on rocks and old walls; leaves without
stipules, long-stalked, reniform, shortly and very broadly 5-lobed,
the lobes slightly pointed, glabrous, frequently tinged with purple
below; flowers axillary, solitary; calyx 5-lobed nearly to the
base, lobes narrow, glabrous; corolla (A, laid open × 2) lilac,
the tube streaked with crimson-purple, the two humps on
the lower side of the lip tinged with orange and closing the
spurred tube; on the lower side of the tube a dense carpet of

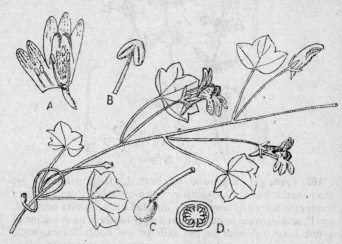

stiff inwardly directed hairs; stamens (B, × 3) 4, 2 longer and 2
shorter; stalks of longer stamens hairy at the base; ovary
(C, × 3) deep crimson, 2-locular, with numerous ovules attached
to the middle (D, × 6); style thick and undivided; fruit a globose capsule with several warted seeds (family *Scrophulariaceae*).
  This pretty little plant flowers from the late spring until the
autumn. Growing on old dry walls and rocks it is remarkably
resistant to drought. The flowers are adapted to the visits of bees
who are able to press down the lower lip and gain access to the
nectar, which is secreted around the fleshy base of the ovary and
stored in the spur at the bottom of the corolla. After fertilisation
takes place the flower stalks curve towards dark crevices in the
wall where the seeds are deposited when the fruit ripens and bursts.

182. Herb Robert, *Geranium robertianum* L. ($\times \frac{2}{5}$); much branched annual; stems sprinkled with slender hairs, often turning bright red and with a disagreeable smell when rubbed; leaves opposite, pinnately divided into three main segments, these again deeply divided, sprinkled with a few weak setose hairs on both sides; petioles long; stipules ovate - lanceolate, hairy; flowers few on a long axillary peduncle; sepals (A, $\times$ 3) narrowly oblong, conspicuously 3-nerved, notched at the apex and with a long slender point; petals (B,

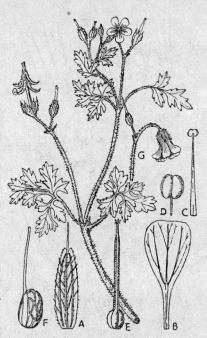

$\times$ 2¼) broadly spoon-shaped, reddish-purple to white or pink; stamens 10 (C, $\times$ 3), anthers (D, $\times$ 5) suborbicular; ovary (E, $\times$ 4) deeply 5-grooved, with a stiff erect hairy style and 5 small stigmas; fruiting carpels (F, $\times$ 3) covered with a coarse network; easily recognised from the less common species by the deeply divided leaves (family *Geraniaceae*).

Nectar is secreted only outside the base of the five inner stamens, which are the first to open their anthers and shed their pollen. They are then in the middle of the flower with the stigmas above them, and insect visitors are dusted with the pollen which they transfer to the stigmas of another flower. The five outer stamens are at first curved widely outwards, but later they move towards the middle of the flower and likewise discharge their pollen. Self-pollination, however, is not impossible, owing to the flower, which is normally erect in daytime, being pendulous at night (fig. G) or during bad weather.

183. Stork's Bill, *Erodium cicutarium* (L.) L'Hérit. ($\times \frac{2}{5}$); annual or biennial, covered with weak spreading hairs; radical leaves (A, $\times \frac{3}{5}$) on long stalks, pinnately divided with the segments deeply cut; stem-leaves opposite, markedly unequal-sized in each pair (anisophyllous), much divided; peduncles long and slender, bearing an umbel of few small flowers from a whorl of small bracts; stalks very slender; sepals (B, $\times$ 3) oblong, with short bristly hairs outside and a sharp horn at the tip; petals (C, $\times$ 4) purple or pink, hairy at the base; stamens 5, with 5 rudimentary; ovary (D, $\times$ 4) deeply lobed, hairy, topped by a columnar style and 5 connate stigmas; carpels (E, $\times \frac{4}{5}$) elongating into long beaks in fruit which separate from the central axis and become spirally twisted, falling and penetrating the soil (family *Geraniaceae*).

Only the five stamens opposite to the sepals bear anthers, those opposite the petals being broader and without anthers. Only those with anthers have nectaries at their bases. The character of the unequal-sized leaves is very rare among British plants, though much more common amongst other tropical species which are crowded in dense forests.

Pollination of this species has been much studied on the continent; two forms, that figured here which opens its flowers at about 7 a.m., is self-pollinated and sheds its petals by midday, and another (*pimpinellifolium*) cross-pollinated by insects and whose petals last until the second day.

184. Wood-Sorrel, *Oxalis acetosella* L. (× ⅘); perennial with a short creeping rootstock, knotted here and there with thickened hairy scales; leaves all radical, with long slender stalks, completely divided into 3 rounded-obovate leaflets notched at the apex and wedge-shaped at the base, very thin, sprinkled on both surfaces with long rather stiff hairs; nerves radiating from the base of the leaflet; flowers single on long slender stalks longer than the leaves; stalks bearing a pair of bracts about half-way up and these fringed with hairs; sepals 5, obovate, slightly pubescent; petals free, white, obovate, notched at the apex, about ½-in. long; stamens (A, × 3) 10; ovary (B, × 3) 5-locular, with 5 almost separate styles, with several ovules in each loculus attached to the central axis; fruit an ovoid capsule, with 2 shining black seeds in each of the 5 compartments (family *Oxalidaceae*).

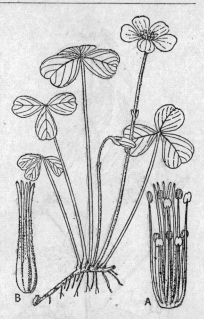

If cows eat this plant it may be the cause of serious illness and diarrhoea, and in the case of sheep even be fatal. It is recorded that the milk of cows after having eaten it is with difficulty converted into butter. They are only liable to encounter it, however, if turned out into woodlands where it grows. It flowers in early spring, and is believed to be the original of the Irish Shamrock, though that emblem is now transferred to a clover, *Trifolium repens* (fig. 26), which has rather similar leaves. The white petals are streaked with violet lines, which serve as nectar-guides, and there is a yellow spot above the nectaries which are borne on the claws of the petals.

185. Evergreen Alkanet, *Anchusa sempervirens* L. ($\times \frac{1}{4}$); perennial remaining leafy through the winter; leaves alternate, luscious green, broadly ovate, pointed at the apex, rounded at the base, covered like the rest of the plant with stiff hairs; flowers (A, $\times \frac{1}{2}$) small, arranged in one-sided clusters on short axillary branches; calyx (C, $\times \frac{1}{2}$) deeply 5-lobed, lobes fringed with hairs; corolla (B, $\times \frac{3}{4}$) a lovely deep sky-blue with a white "eye"; stamens 5, included in the corolla-tube; ovary (C, $\times \frac{1}{2}$) deeply divided into 4 rounded lobes with the columnar style between them; fruitlets (D, $\times \frac{3}{4}$) 4, reticulate; grows in waste places (family *Boraginaceae*).

A very beautiful plant with Forget-me-not-like deep sky-blue flowers with a white "eye." Common in south-west Europe, and in south-west England, and in some places makes a delightful display in the hedgerows. In other parts it is usually found around villages and houses, sometimes invading gardens, as it has done recently in the Kew neighbourhood. It flowers during spring and the first half of the summer, with crop after crop of blooms on the same plant.

186. Water Forget-Me-Not, *Myosotis palustris* Hill ($\times \frac{2}{3}$); perennial with creeping or suberect rootstock; stems ascending, rounded, with appressed hairs; leaves alternate, narrowly oblong or oblanceolate, blunt or rounded at the apex, narrowed to the base and sessile, faintly nerved, the nerves looped well within the margin, clothed on both surfaces with very short stiff bulbous-based hairs; flowers in a 2-forked 1-sided inflorescence (scorpioid cyme) the branches of which are coiled in the bud stage at the tip; no bracts; calyx (A, $\times$ 3) bell-shaped, shortly 5-

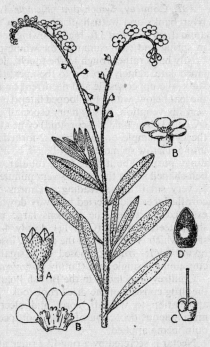

toothed, loosely covered with very short stiff hairs; corolla (B, $\times \frac{2}{3}$) bright clear blue with a yellow "eye"; rather large (for the genus) and showy, with a small straight tube partly closed at its mouth by 5 scales, and a spreading 5-lobed limb; stamens 5, hidden in the tube, alternate with the corolla lobes; ovary (C, $\times$ 4) vertically divided into 4 lobes, with the unbranched style inserted between the lobes (gynobasic); nutlets (D, $\times$ 4) ovoid, slightly compressed, with a sharp margin, black and highly polished (family *Boraginaceae*).

Grows in wet ditches and by the sides of streams and flowers all the summer; easily separated from nearly all the other British species, of which there are several, by the calyx which is only toothed, and not deeply lobed as in the others. *M. repens* Don is very close, but has the calyx cut half-way down into narrow lobes, and *M. caespitosa* Schultz has a very small corolla.

187. Comfrey, *Symphytum officinale* L. ($\times \frac{1}{2}$); perennial on river banks and wettish places, with a thick rootstock; stems annual, up to about 3 ft. high, growing very rapidly and flowering in spring and early summer, the whole plant clothed with pale bristly hairs rather rough to the touch; leaves alternate, broadly lanceolate, acutely tapered to the apex, the lower with a winged stalk, the upper sessile and decurrent on the stem often as far as the leaf below, with a few looped lateral nerves on each side and a very lax venation, bristly hairy especially on the nerves; flowers (A, $\times 1\frac{1}{4}$) in a 1-sided (scorpioid) cyme at the ends of the shoots, the cyme simple or sometimes 2-forked; calyx deeply divided into 5 narrow segments; corolla (B, $\times 1\frac{1}{4}$) pale yellow, white or dingy purple, about $\frac{2}{3}$ in. long, tubular, the tube expanded and bell-shaped about the middle, very minutely hairy outside; lobes 5, very small and spreading; stamens 5, alternating with the corolla-lobes and inserted half-way down the tube; anthers not exserted; between the stamens large processes margined by sharp teeth; ovary (C, $\times 1\frac{1}{4}$) deeply 4-lobed, with the simple style, which is longer than the corolla, inserted between the lobes (gynobasic); fruit composed of 4 small smooth nutlets each containing a single seed (family *Boraginaceae*).

Comfrey is included in the British Pharmaceutical Codex, and the drug consists of the dried rootstock. It has been used as an application to wounds, sores and ulcers of various kinds, a mucilaginous decoction of fresh root, peeled and bruised into a pulp, being applied.

Nectar is secreted by a ring-like ridge at the base of the ovary, and stored in the base of the corolla. Automatic self-pollination is inevitable because the flowers hang down, the stigma being brought into line with the pollen. Within the corolla and between the anthers are 5 large processes which are margined with sharp teeth (like miniature shark's teeth), and these teeth prevent insect visitors from probing for nectar between the filaments, and they are obliged to insert their proboscis in such a way that it gets dusted with pollen.

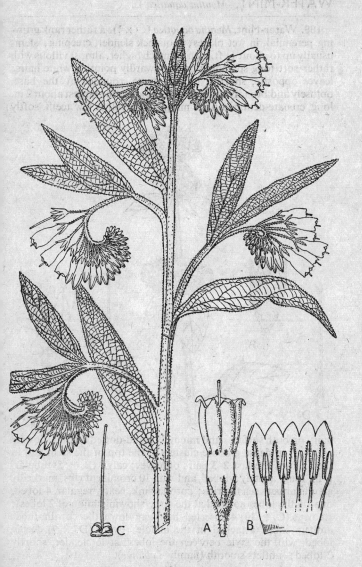

**188. Water-Mint, *Mentha aquatica* L. ($\times \frac{1}{2}$); a rather rank grow-ing perennial, in wet places; rootstock slender, creeping; stems usually up to about 1½ ft. high, or much higher, almost villous with rather soft long spreading or downwardly pointing white hairs; leaves opposite, shortly stalked, ovate, rounded at the base, obtusely and broadly triangular at the apex, the largest about 2 in. long, crenate-dentate on the margin with rather few teeth, softly

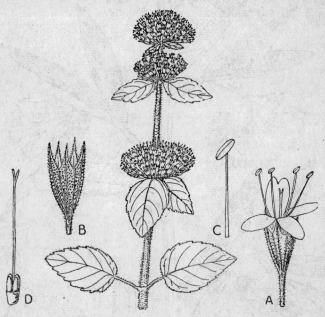

hairy on both surfaces and minutely gland-dotted below; flowers (A, $\times$ 3) in dense globose clusters at the top of the stem and in the axils of the last 2–3 pairs of leaves; calyx (B, $\times$ 5) tubular, $\frac{1}{6}$ in. long, acutely 5-lobed, and with 10 prominent ribs, markedly glandular between the ribs; corolla pink, nearly regular, 4-lobed, one of the lobes notched at the apex (showing union of 2 lobes); stamens (C, $\times$ 10) 4, inserted half-way down the corolla-tube; anthers short, attached in the middle; ovary (D, $\times$ 7) deeply lobed, with the style between the lobes; style slender, shortly 2-lobed; nutlets smooth (family *Labiatae*).

189. Wood-Sage, *Teucrium scorodonia* L. (× ⅖); perennial with a creeping rootstock; 4-angled softly hairy stems up to 2 ft. high; leaves shortly stalked, ovate to oblong-lanceolate, cordate at the base, with a short triangular apex, 1½–2 in. long, coarsely toothed, markedly wrinkled (bullate), hairy, closely and minutely glandular below; flowers (A, × 1¼) in slender terminal racemes,

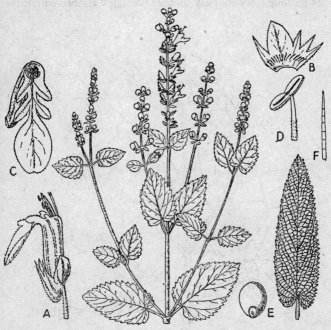

all forming a loose panicle with the flowers all to one side; upper leaves gradually reduced to bracts; each leafy bract with a single flower in its axil; stalks very short; calyx (B, × 1½) unequally 5-toothed, the upper tooth broad and ovate, turned back, strongly nerved in fruit, with a ring of long deflexed several-celled hairs inside (F, enlarged); corolla yellow (C, × 1¼) 1-lipped, lip unequally 5-lobed folded over the stamens within the tube; stamens (D, × 10) 4, inserted half-way down the tube, anther-lobes opening by one continuous slit; ovary deeply 4-lobed; nectariferous disk large and cupular (family *Labiatae*).

190. Hedge Stachys, *Stachys sylvatica* L. ($\times \frac{1}{2}$); perennial; rootstock with stolons; stem stout, quadrangular, up to 4 ft. high, rather densely hispid with whitish stiff hairs; leaves very much like those of the common stinging nettle, the basal ones sometimes as large; stem leaves opposite, stalked, broadly ovate, cordate at the base, with a broad triangular apex, averaging about 2½ in. long, very coarsely toothed (dentate), clothed with rather

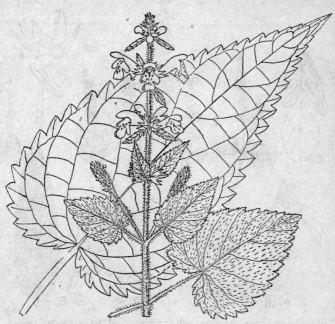

long stiffish hairs; flowers in whorls of about 6 to 10, the upper becoming more crowded, the leaves gradually reduced to bracts; calyx equally 5-lobed, lobes triangular, acute, glandular hairy outside; corolla dark reddish-purple, 2-lipped, upper lip forming a hood over the stamens and undivided, lower lip 3-lobed, the middle lobe notched; tube contracted and with a ring of hairs inside near the base; stamens 4, under the upper lip; filaments hairy; ovary deeply 4-lobed, with the style between the lobes; nutlets smooth, rounded at the top (family *Labiatae*).

191. Red Dead-Nettle, *Lamium purpureum* L. (× ½); annual or biennial, flowering more or less the whole season, usually found as a garden weed and in waste places; stems spreading and ascending, square in section, pubescent with short reflexed hairs; leaves opposite, the lower on stalks longer than the blade and fringed with rather long weak hairs, the upper with very short stalks; blade ovate, rather widely cordate at the base, coarsely toothed (crenate-serrate), very undulate (bullate) on the upper surface and coarsely reticulate; stalks connected across the stem; calyx

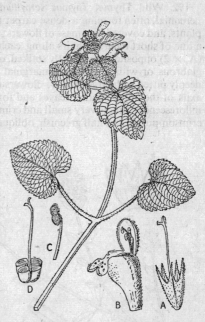

(A, × 3) equally 5-lobed to about the middle, tinged with crimson, the lobes awl-shaped (subulate), shortly hairy; corolla (B, × 1½) 2-lipped, deep mauve-pink, the upper lobe undivided and forming a hood over the 4 stamens (C, × 4) with deep orange pollen, the 2 side lobes very small and narrow, the front lobe deeply split into two parts and mottled with deep crimson like the spotted orchid; anthers hairy; ovary (D, × 6) deeply divided into 4 parts with flat (truncate) tops, with the style arising from the base (gynobasic); fruit composed of 4 similar little nuts, each with a single seed; there are four other species of this genus in Britain, *Lamium album* L. with white corolla, *L. amplexicaule* L., with purplish red corolla with a slender tube, *L. maculatum* L. resembling *L. album* but with a red corolla and a ring of hairs in the tube, and *L. galeobdolon* Crantz, with a yellow corolla (family *Labiatae*).

192. Wild Thyme, *Thymus serpyllum* L. (aggregate) ($\times \frac{2}{5}$); perennial, often forming a dense carpet to the exclusion of other plants, and covered by a mass of flowers; stems wiry, slender, with a line of short recurved hairs along each of the 4 angles; leaves (A, $\times$ 2) opposite, very shortly stalked, ovate, oblong or obovate, glabrous or with a few long marginal hairs towards the base, deeply pitted with large glands; flowers (B, $\times$ 3) in whorls in the axils of the upper smaller leaves and forming a dense spike-like inflorescence; bracts very small and crimson; calyx (C, $\times$ 3) half crimson-purple and half greenish, obliquely bell-shaped, 2-lipped,

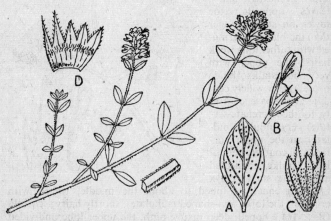

the upper lip broad and with 3 ovate teeth, the lower of 2 narrow awl-shaped lobes, 10-ribbed, hairy and minutely glandular outside, with a ring of hairs inside which closes over the nutlets in fruit; corolla pink, short and broad, 2-lipped, the upper lip broad and notched, the lower 3-lobed; stamens 4, as long as the corolla; ovary deeply 4-lobed, with the bifid style between the lobes; nutlets dark brown; smooth (family *Labiatae*).

On dry grassy banks, flowering in summer. The flowers are much visited by insects. A general favourite, for most people "Know a bank whereon the Wild Thyme blows." After the corollas have dropped off a ring of hairs inside the top of the calyx-tube (D, $\times$ 3) spreads over the little nutlets.

193. Hemp-Nettle, *Galeopsis tetrahit* **L.** ($\times \frac{2}{5}$); a coarse-growing annual up to about 2½ ft. high, with a succulent stem thickened below the nodes, more or less branched, and clothed with very stiff jointed bristly hairs especially below the nodes, and with here and there a few shorter gland-tipped hairs (A, $\times 1\frac{1}{4}$); leaves fairly long-stalked, ovate to ovate-lanceolate, rounded to wedge-shaped at the base, broadly pointed at the top, coarsely

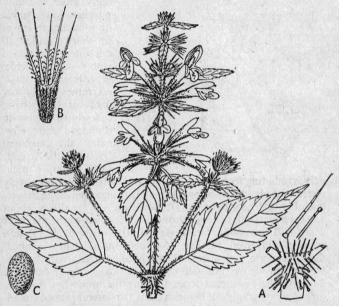

toothed (crenate-serrate) (except the rounded base), clothed with scattered long stiff hairs especially on the upper surface; flowers arranged in dense clusters in the axils of the upper leaves and leafy bracts, sessile; calyx (B, $\times 2\frac{1}{4}$) ribbed, divided into 5 equal long very sharp prickle-like lobes, pubescent outside; corolla pale purple or white, with a narrow very pubescent tube and markedly 2-lipped, the upper lip suberect, entire, the lower lip spreading and 3-lobed; stamens 4, in pairs under the upper lip; anthers bordered with minute hairs; ovary deeply lobed; nutlets (C, $\times 2\frac{1}{4}$) obovoid, brown, sprinkled with a paler lace-like layer (family *Labiatae*).

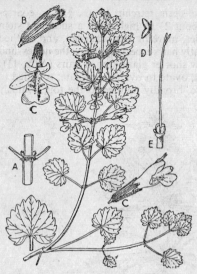

194. Ground Ivy, *Nepeta hederacea* (L.) Trev. ($\times$ $\frac{2}{3}$); perennial with stems creeping at the base and rooting at the nodes; stems 4-angled, very minutely hairy, green and dull-purplish; lower leaves on long, upper leaves on shorter stalks, all opposite, often tinged with dull purple, broadly ovate-rounded, rather widely cordate at the base, coarsely toothed with rounded teeth (crenate) the terminal " tooth " the largest, with about 7 main nerves radiating from the base, very minutely hairy above, finely pitted with gland dots below; leaf-stalks connected at the base by line of long slender hairs (A, $\frac{4}{5}$); flowers (C, $\times$ $\frac{4}{5}$) axillary, about 3 in each leaf-axil, the middle one flowering first whilst the other 2 are still tiny buds; stalk very short; calyx (B, $\times$ $1\frac{1}{4}$) dull crimson and green, tubular, 15-ribbed, shortly hairy, 5-lobed, the lobes ovate, very acute and nearly equal-sized; corolla blue, blotched inside the tube with crimson, twice as long as the calyx, 2-lipped, the two upper lobes forming the upper lip, with the forked style sticking out between them, two lateral rounded lobes, the lowermost lobe forming the lower lip and rather widely notched, with numerous stiff rod-like hairs across the mouth of the tube; stamens 4, in pairs under the upper lip, the upper pair the longest; filament produced beyond the gaping anther (D, $\times$ 3) ovary (E, $\times$ 2) deeply and vertically lobed; style not hairy; fruit of four 1-seeded nutlets (family *Labiatae*).

A very charming little plant, the great beauty of whose flowers is best seen with a strong hand-lens; blooms in early spring, and widely distributed in north temperate regions; nectar is secreted at the base of the ovary. Another name is *Nepeta glechoma* Benth.

195. Self-Heal, *Prunella vulgaris* L. (× ⅖); perennial, with slender creeping rootstock; stems annual, up to about a foot high according to situation, sometimes only a few inches, decumbent at the base and rooting at the nodes; stems square in section, often crimson-tinged, more or less hairy; leaves opposite, shortly stalked, ovate-lanceolate, not pointed at the apex, rather broadly wedge-shaped at the base, with about 3 pairs of lateral nerves and entire or obscurely toothed, thinly covered on both surfaces with several-celled hairs; flowers in short terminal spikes which often

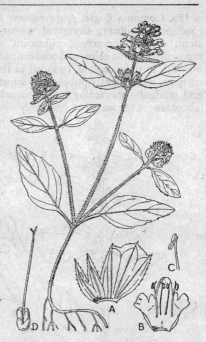

lengthen considerably, subtended by a pair of almost sessile leaves, each whorl of flowers in the axils of very broad large leafy pointed bracts; calyx (A, × 2) 2-lipped, crimson, the upper lip flat and broad, 3-toothed, the lower lip deeply 2-lobed and smaller, with a few longish hairs; corolla (B, × 1¼) violet-purple, 2-lipped, the upper lip erect and hood-like, almost entire, the lower lip spreading and unequally 3-lobed, the middle lobe toothed; stamens (C, × 3) 4, in pairs under the upper lip, each filament produced into a tooth beyond the anther; ovary (D, × 3) vertically and deeply 4-lobed; style slender, shortly 2-lobed; fruit of 4 angular nutlets (family *Labiatae*).

Flowers from late spring until the autumn and grows in fields, banksides, etc.; one of the most widely distributed of our native species, even being found on some of the mountains of the tropics, and showing considerable variation in the size and colour of the flowers.

COMMON BUGLE, *Ajuga reptans* L.

196. **Common Bugle**, *Ajuga reptans* L. ($\times \frac{2}{5}$); perennial, the rootstock producing elongated runner-like stolons; flowering stems erect, unbranched, pubescent with weak white hairs, especially in a line below and between the leaf-bases; lower leaves obovate to oblanceolate, rounded at the apex, and with wavy margins, very slightly pubescent; upper leaves becoming sessile and gradually shortening into coloured bracts, obovate to oblanceolate, with wavy or obscurely toothed margins; flowers

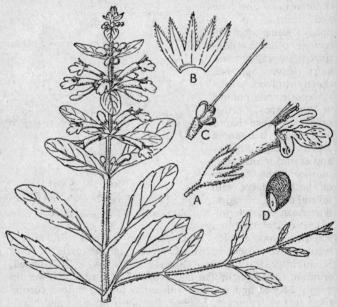

(A, $\times$ 3) in close whorls in the axils of most of the leaves, nearly sessile, the upper ones forming a slightly interrupted spike-like inflorescence; calyx (B, $\times$ 3) equally 5-lobed to about the middle, fringed with jointed hairs; corolla blue, or rarely pink or white, marked with brighter coloured lines, 1-lipped, lip spreading and 3-lobed, the middle lobe largest; stamens 4, anthers exserted; ovary deeply lobed, with a large fleshy gland in front (C, $\times$ 3); style exserted, 2-fid; nutlets reticulate, with a large lateral scar (family *Labiatae*). Grows in fields and grassy open spaces in woods, sometimes in deep shade.

197. Water Plantain, *Alisma plantago-aquatica* L. (× ⅖); aquatic herb, erect and growing in the mud at the bottom of the water; rootstock perennial, bulb-like with the thickened bases of the leaf-stalks; leaves all from the base but with their blades mostly clear of the water, long-stalked, the normally well-developed more or less elliptic-ovate, bluntly pointed at the apex, mostly rounded and somewhat unequal-sided at the base, entire, with a broad flat midrib and 3 or 4 marked longitudinal nerves running parallel from the base to the apex; transverse nerves numerous, conspicuous, rather oblique; flowers small and numerous in a large lax much-branched pyramidal panicle; bracts lanceolate, acute, in whorls; stalks slender, in little clusters; sepals 3, green; petals 3, quite distinct from the sepals, a delicate pale rose colour; stamens (A, × 1½) 6; carpels (B, × 2) numerous, small and 1-seeded, arranged in a single ring on a broad flat axis (C, × ¾) (family *Alismataceae*).

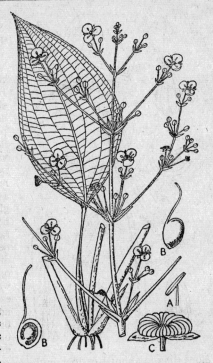

Attention is called in the description of the Spearwort Buttercup (fig. 70) to the close relationship between the family *Alismataceae* and the *Ranunculaceae*. This is evident if the flowers and fruits are compared, in both families there being free sepals, petals and stamens, and several or numerous free carpels. *Alismataceae* is therefore of great botanical interest as it shows a link between the two groups, *Dicotyledons* and *Monocotyledons*.

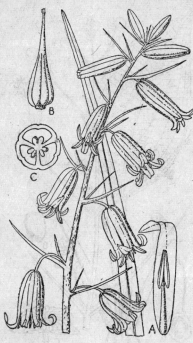

198. Bluebell (English), *Scilla nonscripta* (L.) Hoffmgg. ($\times \frac{4}{5}$); bulb white, full of juice; leaves several, basal, linear, up to a foot long and $\frac{1}{2}$-in. broad, bright green and shining, widely V-shaped and with a rather broad prominent midrib below; flowering stem leafless, varying in height according to exposure to light, normally about 9 in. to a foot high, very juicy, glabrous and shining, bearing at the top a raceme of about a dozen beautifully sky-blue nodding bell-shaped flowers opening from below upwards; at the base of each stalk a pair of unequal-sized narrow bracts, bluish purple; buds at first erect and almost stalkless, the stalk elongating to about $\frac{1}{2}$-in. long in the mature flowers, these about $\frac{3}{4}$-in. long and composed of 6 perianth segments (A, $\times 1\frac{1}{4}$) arranged in 2 series, free to the base and with recurved tops; stamens 6, 3 long and 3 shorter, the 3 longer opening first; filaments attached above the base of the segments, blue; anthers white and rather large; ovary (B, $\times 2$) above the perianth (superior), blue like the perianth, 3-locular and 3-lobed, in each compartment 2 rows of ovules attached to the central axis (C, $\times 4$); fruit a capsule; seeds black (family *Liliaceae*).

Kew Gardens is justly famed for its bluebells which are usually at their best about the first week in May. Large areas are planted with this beautiful flower, and the sea of colour beneath the beech and birch trees just breaking into leaf is worth travelling a long way to see. The species is found wild only in the western part of Europe, extending east along the Mediterranean to Italy.

199. Ramsons, *Allium ursinum* L. ($\times \frac{1}{4}$); bulb ellipsoid, about 2 in. long; leaves very shortly sheathing the flowering stem at the base, long-stalked, flat and broadly lanceolate, about 8 in. long, and 3 in. broad, contracted at the base, with several parallel nerves running from the base to apex, and with oblique secondary veins between (A, $\times$ 3); flowering stem up to about a foot high, leafless, bearing a loose umbel of about a dozen white flowers; bracts rather large and lanceolate, soon withering and falling off; flower-stalks up to about 1 in. long, slender; perianth segments (B, $\times \frac{4}{5}$) 6, lanceolate, acute, spreading; stamens (C, $\times 1\frac{3}{4}$) 6, shorter than and opposite to the segments; anthers (D, $\times$ 3) ovoid; ovary (E, $\times$ 2) above the perianth (superior), 3-lobed, with a rod-like simple style, 3-locular, with several ovules in each compartment arranged in 2 rows on the central axis (F, $\times$ 2); fruit (G, $\times \frac{2}{5}$) deeply 3-lobed, with a black rounded transversely pitted seed (H, $\times$ 3) in each lobe (family *Amaryllidaceae*).

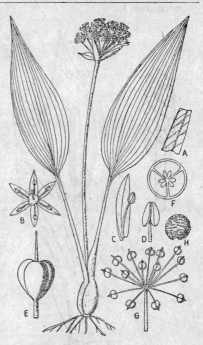

This plant is often very abundant in woods and shady places, sometimes covering all the ground where it grows. It flowers in spring and early summer. Readers who have studied a little botany may wonder why it is placed here in the *Amaryllis* family instead of in the Lily family, where it is to be found in text-books. The only difference between these two families as hitherto defined was that the ovary in the former family is inferior, and in the latter superior. The author, however, considers the nature of the inflorescence a better character, that of the *Amaryllis* family being an umbel, and of the Lily family a spike, raceme or panicle.

LORDS AND LADIES, CUCKOO PINT, *Arum maculatum* L.

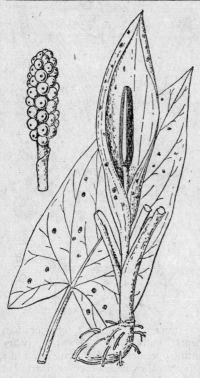

200. Lords and Ladies, Cuckoo Pint, *Arum maculatum* L. ($\times \frac{2}{5}$); rootstock a white tuber; leaves long-stalked, ovate, arrow-shaped at the base, dark shining green, often spotted with purple or streaked with lighter colour; flowers arranged on a long fleshy axis (spadix) enclosed in a large green and purple sheath (spathe) folded over the edges and 6 or more inches long, tapered at the top; upper part of the axis barren and bright purple; lower part bearing the flowers which are unisexual, the upper cluster being male and crowded in a dense mass, each consisting of a single stamen, the lower flowers female, each of a single carpel; above each cluster are a few abortive flowers reduced to hair-like structures, those above the male being longer and directed downwards; berries red (family *Araceae*).

The spathe and the dark red upper end of the spadix attract small insects such as small midges, a further inducement for them being the decomposing, urinous smell. These small creatures creep down between the downwardly directed stiff hairs mentioned above and are trapped by them for a time. They thus deposit pollen from another spadix upon the already receptive stigmas of the female flowers at the bottom. Whilst they are trapped, pollen falls in a shower from the stamens above and dusts the insects with a fresh supply.

201. Yellow Flag, *Iris pseudacorus* L. ($\times \frac{1}{2}$); perennial, with a thick horizontal rootstock; flowering stem up to about 2 ft. high; lower leaves often longer, up to 2 in. broad, all in one plane (equitant), pale green, the upper leaves becoming much shorter; flowers large and bright yellow, 2–3 at the top of each stem, appearing one at a time from a sheathing bract; outer perianth-segments recurved, broadly obovate, narrowed to the base, with a deeper band across the middle, the inner segments oblong-lanceolate, erect, very much smaller than the outer; stamens (A, $\times 1\frac{1}{2}$) 3, opposite the petal-like stigmas and hidden by them; anthers large; ovary below the perianth (inferior), 3-locular (B, $\times 1\frac{1}{2}$), with numerous ovules attached to the middle; stigmas petal-like, alternate with the inner perianth-segments, split into 2 at the top, with a short scale-like appendage inside; fruit a capsule up to 3 in. long; seeds numerous, pale green (family *Iridaceae*).

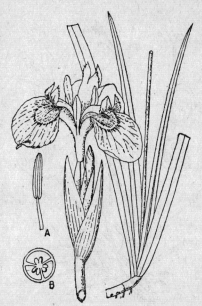

This beautiful plant grows in wet places and by the side of watercourses and is widely spread in Europe and Russian Asia. It flowers in summer and is one of the most handsome of our wild flowers and worthy of a place in a bog garden. A second species, *Iris foetidissima* L., is much less common and mostly found in southern counties. Its flowers are violent-blue or whitish, the capsules with their bright orange or scarlet seeds being very conspicuous and ornamental during the autumn.

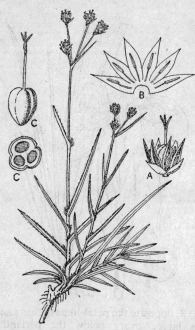

202. Field Woodrush, *Luzula campestris* L. ($\times \frac{2}{5}$); perennial herb, up to about 1 ft. high, with rather slender root-stock; old leaf-bases persistent; leaves linear, 1-nerved, mostly at the base of the plant, the margins fringed with long weak hairs, completely sheathing around the stem at the base and with a bunch of long hairs at the top of the sheath; flowers (A, $\times 1\frac{1}{2}$) collected into head-like clusters, usually from 3–6 together at the top of the slender stems; the middle cluster very shortly stalked or almost sessile, the others on much longer stalks; bracts below each flower rather large, membranous, triangular-ovate, fringed with hairs; perianth-segments (B, $\times 2\frac{1}{2}$) 6, rich dark brown with pale thin shining margins, ovate-lanceolate and very acutely pointed; stamens 6, opposite the perianth-segments; anthers linear, attached at the base, opening inwards (introrse); ovary (C, $\times 4$) 3-lobed, 1-locular with 3 erect ovules attached at the base; style divided into 3 greenish white hairy stigmas which twist together into a spiral after flowering; capsule triangular, with 3 erect seeds (family *Juncaceae*).

A very common plant, flowering in spring, in rather dry fields, woods and heaths, and widely distributed in temperate regions all over the world. A very similar species is *L. spicata* DC., but this has smaller flowers in *sessile* clusters, collectively forming a spike, is a mountain species from northern districts, and flowers in summer. Flowers of this family are anemophilous, i.e. the pollen is blown about by the wind, though they are not unisexual.

GLOSSARY OF BOTANICAL TERMS

ACHENE: a small, dry seed-like fruit.

acuminate: gradually pointed.

adnate: attached the whole length to another structure.

alternate: not opposite to something else.

annual: lasting only one year or season.

anther: portion of stamen bearing the pollen.

apiculate: with a little point.

aquatic: living in water.

aril: outgrowth from seed-stalk (common in *Euphorbia* family).

astringent: contracting or binding.

axil: the angle between leaf and branch or stem.

axillary: in the axil.

berry: succulent fruit with seeds immersed in the pulp.

biennial: lasting two years.

bisexual: having two sexes (*i.e.*, stamens and pistil in the same flower).

bract: modified leaf at base of flower-stalk or leaves around a flower-head.

bracteole: small bract on the flower stalk.

bullate: blistered or puckered.

calcareous: chalky or limey.

calyx: outermost, usually green floral envelope.

capitate: arranged in a head, or head-like.

capsule: dry fruit which opens.

carpel: one or more divisions of ovary or fruit.

caruncle: wart or protuberance near stalk of seed.

catkin: slender, often pendulous spike of flowers.

compound: formed of many similar parts.

concave: scooped out.

connective: portion of filament connecting lobes of the anther.

connate: united similar parts.

convex: humped.

cordate: heart-shaped.

corolla: collective name for the petals.

corymb: more or less flat-topped collection of flowers.

crenate: with blunt, curved teeth.

crenulate: diminutive of crenate.

cross-pollination: transference of pollen from one flower to stigmas of another.

cyme: an inflorescence repeatedly divided with the oldest flower in the middle of each fork.

cystoliths: mineral markings in the leaves as found in the Nettle family.

deciduous: falling off.

decumbent: lying on the ground.

decurrent: running down.

dentate: toothed.

dioecious: male and female flowers on different trees.

disk: a fleshy portion of floral axis, often secreting nectar.

disk-flower: flowers in the middle of a flower head with rays.

drupe: stone fruit such as a plum.

elliptic: shaped like an ellipse.

endosperm: reserve food material in a seed.

entire: not divided or toothed.

epicalyx: collection of bracteoles like an extra calyx.

falcate: sickle-shaped.

female: the fruiting part of the flower (ovary or carpels).

247

GLOSSARY OF BOTANICAL TERMS

filament: stalk of stamen.
fruit: the fertilized and mature ovary or carpel.

glabrous: not hairy.
glaucous: with a whitish-blue lustre like the " bloom " of a grape.
globose: round like a globe.

hastate: like an arrow, but with the barbs turned outwards.

imbricate: overlapping, with one part wholly outside.
inferior: below.
inflexed: turned inwards.
inflorescence: collection of flowers on the shoot.
introrse: facing inwards.
involucre: a ring of bracts surrounding one or more flowers.
irregular: applied to a flower (like that of a pea) which cannot be divided into equal halves in more than one direction.

lanceolate: lance-shaped.
leaflet: unit of a compound leaf.
lenticels: corky spots on bark.
lobulate: divided into small lobes.
locular: divided into chambers.
loculus: a chamber or cavity of an ovary, fruit, or anther.
longitudinal: lengthwise.

male: a plant or flower which bears stamens.
monoecious: male and female flowers on the same plant.
mucronate: bearing a little tip.

nectary: organ in which nectar is secreted.
node: point of insertion of a leaf or leaves.
nutlet: little nut.

oblanceolate: reverse of lanceolate.
obovate: reverse of ovate.

opposite: inserted at same level, as leaves on a shoot.
orbicular: circular.
ovary: the female part of the flower, represented by the carpels.
ovate: egg-shaped.
ovoid: ovate in outline.
ovule: the organ which after fertilization develops into a seed.

panicle: a branched raceme.
papillous: clothed with short, knob-like hairs.
pappus: modified calyx of the *Compositae*.
pectinate: divided like a comb.
pedicel: the ultimate flower-stalk.
peduncle: common stalk of several flowers.
peltate: attached in the middle (like the stalk of a mushroom).
pendulous: hanging down.
perennial: lasting more than two years.
perianth: the collective outer covering of the flower.
persistent: not falling off.
petal: the usually coloured inner part of the floral leaves.
petiolate: stalked leaves.
petiole: leaf-stalk.
pinnate: divided like a feather.
placenta: the part of the ovary or carpel which bears the ovules.
plumose: feather-like.
pollen: the fertilizing, dust-like powder in the anthers.
procumbent: lying down.
pubescent: hairy.

raceme: unbranched inflorescence with individual flowers stalked.
radical: from the root.
ray-flower: marginal flower of the *Compositae*.
receptacle: floral axis.
reflexed: bent back.
regular: symmetrical.

248

reticulate: like a net.
rootstock: underground stem.

scabrid: rough.
segment: division of an organ.
self-pollination: pollen from the same flower.
serrate: with saw-like teeth.
serrulate: diminutive of serrate.
sessile: without a stalk.
spadix: spike with a fleshy axis (as in *Arum*).
spathe: envelope around the spadix.
spike: stiff unbranched inflorescence with the flowers not stalked.
stamen: the male organ of the flower.
stigma: tip of the style.
stipule: appendage at base of leaf or leaf-stalk.
stolon: basal branch which roots.
style: narrow portion of pistil between ovary and stigma.
superior: placed above.

tendril: thread-like production.
terminal: at the top or end.
ternate: in threes.
tomentose: densely covered with short hairs.
truncate: cut off abruptly.
tuber: fleshy underground part of the stem.
tuberculate: with small outgrowths like warts.

umbel: inflorescence branched like the ribs of an umbrella.
unisexual: of one sex.

valve: portion into which a fruit or other organ separates or opens.
villous: with long shaggy hairs.
viscid: sticky.
vitta: oil tubes of fruits of *Umbelliferae*.

whorl: arranged in a circle around an axis.

INDEX TO COMMON NAMES

(The numbers refer to the illustrations)

INDEX TO COMMON NAMES

INDEX TO COMMON NAMES

INDEX TO NAMES OF GENERA

(The numbers refer to the illustrations)

254

PUFFIN PICTURE BOOKS

This series of children's books contains a number of titles on Natural History. Among them are the following:

One shilling and sixpence each
* Boards only, 2s.6d.